Leonard M.
Practical Distiller

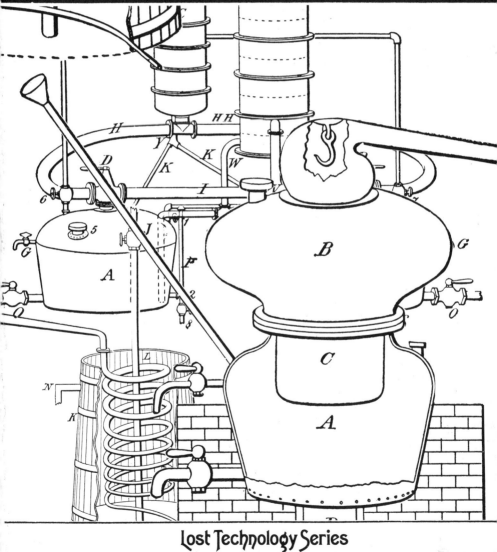

Lost Technology Series
Reprinted by Lindsay Publications Inc.

LEONARD MONZERT'S
Practical Distiller

Leonard Monzert, Professional Distiller and Rectifier

Copyright 1987 by Lindsay Publications, Inc., Bradley, IL 60915. Original copyright, 1889 by Dick & Fitzgerald. Published in New York by Dick & Fitzgerald, and in London by Trubner & Co.

ISBN 0-917914-58-9

2 3 4 5 6 7 8 9 0

MONZERT'S
PRACTICAL DISTILLER

An Exhaustive Treatise on

THE ART OF DISTILLING AND RECTIFYING
SPIRITUOUS LIQUORS AND ALCOHOL

GIVING

Directions for Constructing and Operating the Stills and their
Appurtenances in Present Use; a New Process of Distilla-
tion free from Fusel Oil; the Best Methods for Dis-
tilling Essential Oils, Extracts, Flavorings,
Etc.; the Most Modern Appliances for
the Manufacture of Vinegar; the
Formation and Properties of
Alcohol, with other

VALUABLE INFORMATION

FOR

DISTILLERS, COMPOUNDERS AND LIQUOR DEALERS

INCLUDING

TABLES OF PERCENTAGE, SPECIFIC GRAVITY, ETC.

AND

A Complete Description of the French Apparatus for the
Production of Pure Alcohol by Continuous
Distillation and Rectification

ILLUSTRATED BY NUMEROUS DIAGRAMS

By LEONARD MONZERT
Professional Distiller and Rectifier

WARNING

Remember that the materials and methods described here are from another era. Workers were less safety conscious then, and some methods may be downright dangerous. Be careful! Use good solid judgement in your work, and think ahead. Lindsay Publications, Inc. has not tested these methods and materials and does not endorse them. Our job is merely to pass along to you information from another era. Safety is your responsibility.

Write for a catalog or other unusual books available from:

Lindsay Publications, Inc.
PO Box 12
Bradley, IL 60915-0012

PREFACE.

In presenting this book to the public it is with the intention of conveying, in as brief a manner as is consistent with perspicuity, a clear conception of the methods by which spirituous liquors are obtained and purified. It may be remarked that this work is entirely free from theoretical or undeveloped ideas. Its contents are based upon well established facts which have been obtained by practical experience, and fully demonstrated by the author while acting in his capacity of distiller, rectifier and compounder for over a quarter of a century, during which time many changes have taken place, improvements have been perfected, old theories have been cast aside, important facts have been adduced and verified, and much that was formerly shrouded in mystery has been brought to light.

The construction and management of the Still, its various forms and modifications, from the primitive pots to the complicated alcohol rectifying apparatus, with its tall column and powerful condensers, are all clearly explained.

The distillation of essential oils, the production of flavoring extracts, the formation and purification of alcohol, the proper management of liquors, are all well worthy of consideration. Each subject is treated separately and in a manner which can not be misunderstood.

The author has been specially careful to avoid the introduction of abstruse problems and intricate chemical analysis, as tending to perplex rather than aid the practical operative.

It will be seen upon perusal that this work has been written by one who, although laying no claim to literary ability, is thoroughly conversant with the subjects upon which it treats, and he submits with full confidence the results of his labor to a discerning and appreciative public.

CONTENTS.

PAGE.

CONTENTS.

ILLUSTRATIVE DIAGRAMS.

THE PRACTICAL DISTILLER.

PRELIMINARY OBSERVATIONS.

The production of spirituous liquors, or what may be called the art of converting the substance of plants, seeds and fruit into alcoholic spirits, is a remarkably extensive as well as remunerative industry, not only in the United States, but in nearly all parts of the Civilized World. Every country produces alcoholic spirits of some sort under various denominations, such as Brandy, Gin, Rum, Whiskey, Arrac, Poteen, etc., all of which owe their respective intoxicating properties to the amount of alcohol which they contain.

Brandy (Eau de vie) is the French spirits ; Gin is that of Holland ; Great Britain produces Whiskey ; India, Arrac, and the West Indies, Rum ; while in the United States, liquors of every description are produced in abundance.

These liquors differ in quality and flavor, according to the nature of the material from which they are obtained, as well as the manner of their production.

Fermentation and distillation are the two principal operations by which alcoholic substances are obtained.

Malting and mashing are subservient to these and in many instances are dispensed with altogether.

At what remote period of the world's history distilling became known is only a matter of conjecture. We are told that many centuries ago, when the Alchemist was looked upon as something more than human, a fiery liquid was produced by some Monks which was supposed to possess unlimited curative powers. This was called by them " The Spirit of the Wine," and subsequently "Spirits of Wine" (in French, " Esprit du vin", in German, " Weingeist "), and was employed as a most wonderful medicinal agent.

A century or two afterwards, a hermit in the South of France discovered that by boiling wine in earthen pots, and condensing the vapors, a highly aromatic cordial was obtained; which, when imbibed, produced such stimulating effects that it became known as the " water of life " (*Eau de Vie*).*

This was in all probability the first alcoholic liquor produced ; and, as generation succeeded generation, the crude earthen pots were discarded to make way for the more modern appliance called the Still or Alembic.

Previous to entering into the details of constructing and operating the Still and the manner of obtaining alcoholic liquors, it may be well to offer a few brief remarks, which are intended to serve as a preliminary or rudimentary review of the whole system by which alcoholic products are obtained.

The art of distilling consists of extracting the sugar,

---

* In all parts of France the common name of brandies is *Eau de Vie*.

or what is known as the saccharine matter, which is contained in various vegetable substances, and converting it into alcohol, which is the basis of all intoxicating liquors. This result is obtained by fermenting the juice of grapes, apples, and other fruit and also the extract of grain. The fermenting process differs according to the nature of the material employed.

Grapes and fruit juices contain a natural ferment, which, as soon as exposed to the air, becomes active and produces what appears to be a spontaneous fermentation, which converts the juice into wine. As soon as this transformation is complete, the wine is distilled and the result is brandy.

When grain is employed, as is the case in the manufacture of whiskey, high-wines and alcohol, the system is more complicated ; more skill is required, and a greater amount of vigilance is necessary, than when grapes or other fruits are used.

The substance of grain consists principally of starch. This body is not fermentable, and must therefore be converted into grape-sugar previous to being transformed into alcohol. This is done by the action of a process called " malting."

This newly formed substance is extracted from the grain by another process known as " mashing"; it is then fermented and distilled, and the distillate is whiskey.

These four operations, Malting, Mashing, Fermenting and Distilling will be explained, each under its proper heading.

MALTING.

The first operation toward converting the substance of grain into spirits consists of malting. This in itself is a simple and yet a very tedious process, which must be done in a well-ventilated room.

Put a quantity of barley into a tub; pour cold water over it until the water reaches six inches above the grain. Allow it to remain until it becomes stale and emits a foul odor, then draw it off and replace with fresh water.

Let this stand as before until the grain becomes quite soft, and can be easily pressed between the fingers.

Draw the water off, and pile the grain up on the floor in separate heaps, about ten inches high.

It will be observed that the outside of these heaps soon becomes dry, while the interior becomes warm ; the grain is then turned with great care so as to avoid breaking the seed.

When well mixed (the dry with the wet, the warm with the cold,) pile it up again as before. Repeat this operation every six hours until the germ has grown as long as the seed.

Spread the grain on the floor to the thickness of about two inches; turn it often, in order that it may dry very rapidly.

When dry, remove the germ from the seed by sifting through a sieve coarse enough to allow the germ to pass through but not the seed. When this has been done, dry it again until not a particle of moisture remains.

The result is *Malt* ;—the basis of Ale, Beer, Porter, Whiskey, High-wines and Alcohol. The malt is ground into coarse meal, or crushed, two days before it is required for use.

MASHING.

Pure malt is sometimes employed in the production of liquors ; this however is very seldom the case, especially for whiskey, although it is an acknowledged fact that pure malt makes the best liquor. The usual proportions are, one bushel of malt to from four to seven bushels of unmalted grain ground into coarse meal, and eighteen gallons of water to each bushel of this mixed meal. The water is heated to 160 degrees Fahrenheit and run into a very shallow tub (See *Mash Tub*). Pour in the meal slowly while stirring briskly, and when it is well mixed allow it to stand two hours ; then draw off two-thirds of the water from the meal and replace it by the same quantity that was drawn off, this second water being heated to 180°.

When this second water is well mixed with the grain, it is allowed to stand three-quarters of an hour, and is run off separately from the first.

Repeat this the third time with water heated to 190°, and allow it to stand one hour ; then draw this off from the dregs.

The first drawing is run into cooling pans and as soon as cold enough, is then fermented. The other two are reserved for a second mashing and take the place of the same amount of first water, thus making the subsequent drawing much stronger. This is the system usually employed in making good whiskey.

In making high-wines the whole substance is boiled in order to extract every particle of saccharine matter from the meal; in this case the first and second drawings are run into the fermenting tub together, while the third is reserved to assist in the next mash.

Distillers differ in the manner of performing this operation. Some use more water than others; one may prefer boiling, another will insist that the whole substance can as well be extracted by steeping. One thing, however, can be vouched for;—if quantity is desired without regard to quality, boiling is decidedly the best; but long standing without boiling makes the finest liquor.

THE MASH TUB.

This is a very broad, shallow tub about fifteen feet wide by three feet in height; in the center is an upright revolving shaft, with two or four blades, each one foot wide, extending from the shaft to within three inches of the sides of the tub; (See Diagram No. 1) this is worked by steam or horse power. The blades are perforated with holes, which served to mix the water and meal.

In small distilleries the shaft is worked by hand,

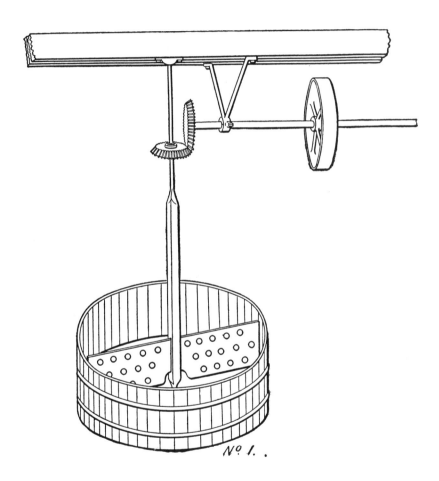

Nº 1.

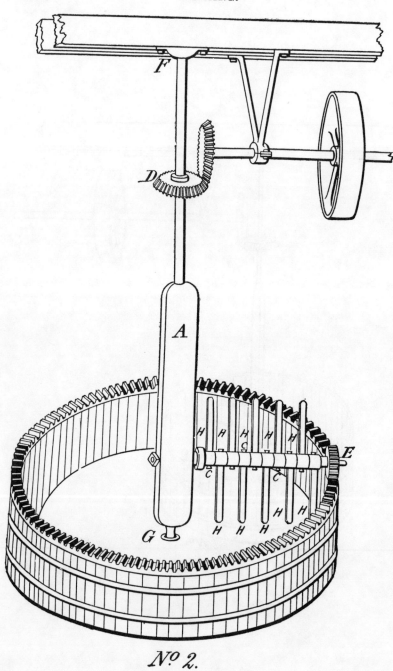

Nº 2.

and in many instances it is dispensed with altogether, the stirring being done with paddles, shaped like an oar, and operated by hand.

In large distilleries, a more effectual apparatus is employed. An upright shaft A (Diagram No. 2) is pivoted in a beam at F and works in a socket G in the centre of the tub's bottom. Four, and sometimes eight, horizontal arms extend at right angles to the upright A ; at the end of each arm is a cog-wheel E which works in slotted gearing which extends around the entire rim of the tub. The arms are supplied with short paddles H H, &c., which reach to within two inches of the bottom of the tub. As the upright revolves the cog-wheel E causes the paddle to revolve in the mash tub as the wheel travels around the rim of the tub. Only one of the four (or eight) arms are shown in the diagram No. 2.

The construction of the horizontal arm and paddles will be better understood by Diagram No. 3.

A is the upright.

B one of the horizontal arms, serving as an axle, and firmly secured to the upright.

C is a tubular collar, fitting on to the axle B, and having a cog-wheel E, securely fastened on the other end.

H is one of the paddles, which fit on the collar C, and are held in place by the screw I.

By this method of construction the collar C with its paddles, revolves freely on the axle B, the paddles revolving rapidly as the wheel E travels around the rim of the tub.

As a precautionary measure it may be well for the

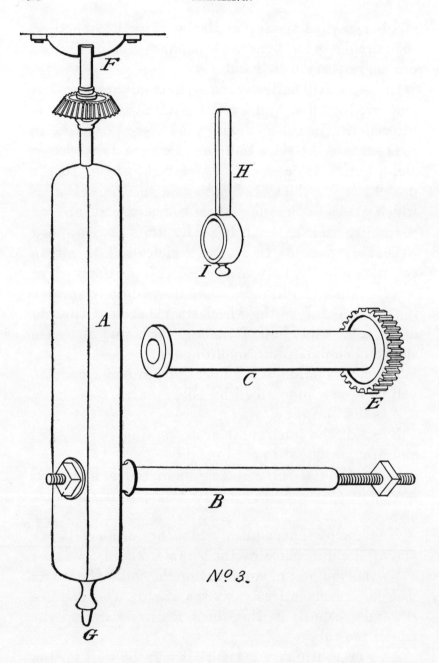

N.º 3.

inexperienced operator to observe the following pre-
cepts in order to insure a successful result.

In heating the water for mashing the grain, the
temperature should conform to the requirements of
the material employed. Pure malt will mix with
much hotter water than unmalted grain ; it is not so
liable to clod up and form into lumps. The proper
temperature is as follows :

For equal portions of ground malt and unmalted
meal, heat the water to 160 degrees, Fahrenheit ;

For one part malt, and two of grain, 150 degrees ;

For one part malt and five of grain, 145 degrees ;

For one part malt to ten of grain, 140 degrees.

The more malt is used the sooner will the wort
clarify. The time required for the liquor to draw
and become clear enough to run into the cooling pans
is from one to two and a half hours.

FERMENTATION OF GRAIN.

Fermentation is the third, and most difficult operation in the whole system. This is the great bug bear
of the distiller, *La Bête Noire*, as the French say.
The practical manner of conducting this operation
will be first shown ; and for the benefit of those who
would become experts, an exhaustive, scientific review will be found on page 91 of this book.

Mix together five bushels of ground malt and
fifteen of corn meal, or other grain not malted. Soak

the lot in hot water (See "*Mashing*") or boil it ; then draw the liquor from the dregs.

Run it into a wide tub, and add to this liquor one gallon of good brewer's yeast, as soon as it has cooled down to 170 degrees.

This will start the fermentation.

The room in which the tub is placed must be kept at a temperature, not less than 65 nor more than 85 degrees.   If the temperature can be raised or lowered so much the better, as the fermentation can be increased or checked at pleasure.

In a short time bubbles of gas will be seen to rise from all parts of this liquor. A ring of froth will form, at first around the edge, then gradually increasing and spreading until it meets in the center, and the whole surface becomes covered with a white creamy foam.

These bubbles rise and break in such numbers that they emit a low hissing sound.   The white foam continues to increase in thickness, breaking into little pointed heaps of a brownish hue on the surface and edges.   This stage of fermentation is called "making yeast."

The yeast gradually thickens, and finally forms a tough viscid crust which, when fermentation slackens, breaks, and falls to the bottom.   In most cases this must be prevented, by skimming it off as soon as the fermentation is complete, which will be indicated by the liquor becoming clear, and the stopping of the hissing noise.

This liquor is then run into the still at once and the distillate is whiskey. (See "*Distilling.*")

THE FERMENTATION OF MOLASSES FOR RUM.

Molasses is employed quite extensively in the production of New England rum.

Take forty gallons New Orleans or West Indies molasses ; add to it two hundred and forty gallons of water heated to 100 degrees Fahrenheit, mix it thoroughly.

Run this mixture into a tub made to hold three hundred gallons, rather broader than high.

Add to this three gallons of fresh brewer's yeast. Keep the temperature in the room as near as possible at 75 degrees.

The fermentation starts rapidly and in course of from 48 to 60 hours, the yeast bubbles will break on the surface, the scum will drop to the bottom and the fermentation is complete.

Run the liquor into the still, distill according to directions and the product is rum.

ACETIC FERMENTATION.

This is the dread of the distiller, the wine maker, and the brewer. When this once sets in, the material is hopelessly lost. It comes with very little warning, and by an inexperienced operator may be very easily and quite likely mistaken for the vinous fermentation. Its presence is detected in the following manner :

When the vinous fermentation is complete, as has already been described, the crust, or yeast, falls to the bottom.   This is the turning point.

If the liquor is not at once drawn off from the sediment, another and far more destructive operation takes place.

The hissing monotonous noise is heard again, the temperature of the liquor rises, a slight inward movement is observable, floating particles appear on the surface and form partly into a jelly cake ; this becomes thicker by degrees, the liquor becomes nearly transparent, the vinous taste disappears, and a sour taste takes its place.   This is caused by the alcohol, which was contained in the liquor at the end of the vinous fermentation, having been converted into vinegar.

FERMENTATION OF GRAPE JUICE, ETC.

In the wine-producing countries, the grapes are gathered and pressed until the whole substance forms a pulp.   This pulp is put into a fermenting tub.

The fermentation starts as soon as the grapes are pressed ; this softens the skins and dissolves a portion of the coloring and astringent matter which the skins, stems and stalks contain.

The liquor is drawn off from the sediment (called in French *Le Marc*) into a clear tub in which it is allowed to ferment until complete.   The proper temperature for fermenting grape juice is 70 degrees Fahrenheit.   The fermented liquor is then distilled in the same manner as whiskey and the result is brandy.

The mark, together with stems and whatever remains after pressing, is then diluted with water, and fermented separately and run through the still into brandy. These two mixed together make a better liquor than either when left separate. It is worthy of note that the grapes which are suitable for wine—making are seldom, if ever, used in the production of brandy.

The fermentation of apple juice, pear juice, berries, etc., is produced in the same manner as grape juice, and requires no artificial means, as it contains its own ferment, which acts spontaneously.

REGULATING FERMENTATION.

A perfect fermentation is the most essential part in the production of all alcoholic distillates ; and in order to ensure success, the following rules must be observed, and should be committed to memory before proceeding to apply them :

1st. The larger the quantity of mash or extract the more perfect will be the fermentation.

2d. A temperature of 65 to 85 degrees is absolutely necessary in the fermenting room.

3d. There must be a sufficient quantity of saccharine matter present.

4th. Fermentation of grain-extract must be started by some active body in a state of decomposition, such as yeast.

5th. There must be water enough to completely dilute the material.

6th. Good ventilation to carry off the gases which are discharged during the process.

When it is found that the operation proceeds too slowly, it will require immediate attention. The best thing, when it can be done, is to increase the temperature in the apartment, then heat some water to a boiling point, fill a lot of bottles with this, and immerse them in the mash or extract.

If the temperature is at the proper degree, then add more yeast to it, mix it well and cover the tub.

Should the fermentation proceed too rapidly, first reduce the temperature in the room, then skim off the head of the yeast. If this does not suffice, draw off the whole into a clean tub.

If any detention should occur, by which fermented liquors cannot be submitted to immediate distillation, the still being, perhaps, undergoing temporary repairs, or for some other reason,—a second fermentation is likely to occur which must be carefully guarded against.

In such case nearly all alkalies, such as lime, pearl ash, chalk, Fuller's earth, etc., may be stirred in the liquor. The fumes of burning sulphur will check fermentation for a while, but will not stop it altogether.

THE STILL AND APPURTENANCES.

The general principles of distilling, although the still has undergone many changes within the present century, is the same now as it was during the time of our great-grand sires.

Evaporation and condensation are the only means by which the different bodies contained in liquids can be separated.

Stills are more or less complicated according to the uses for which they are employed.

The copper still with the worm is the most popular, but some stills are made of wood, others of boiler iron ; and stills ranging from ten to twenty-five gallons capacity, are sometimes made of galvanized iron or heavy tin. These vary in form and shape as well as in the manner of operating them.

Some stills are heated by steam, some by the direct action of the fire underneath, others by being submerged in boiling water.

The larger distilleries usually employ steam for heating. This possesses many advantages over the other methods. It economizes time and fuel, and is safer ; it is also more reliable in maintaining a uniform temperature while conducting the operation.

It is claimed, however, that liquors which are distilled by the direct action of the fire, are superior in quality to those that are produced by steam.

French brandies as well as fine Kentucky whiskeys are products of the ordinary copper still, set in brick work, and in many instances heated by a wood fire.

In order to explain the different methods now in use it is necessary to commence at the bottom and ascend step by step until we reach the pinnacle of the distiller's art ; which is the production of fine inodorous alcohol, free from taste or smell.

PRIMITIVE DISTILLATION.

Stills are sometimes constructed in a rather crude manner, those, for instance that are employed for distilling liquors for home use, or for illicit distilling. These primitive stills are operated in all parts of the country—East, North, South and West. Usually in out of the way places, in caves, barns, cellars or garrets, on barges and canal boats, in the woods, in swamps, and very frequently in some honest farmer's kitchen. One or two such instances will serve to illustrate the more note-worthy of the many contrivances or "make-shifts" which are employed as substitutes for the still.

THE POTEEN STILL.

In many parts of Ireland, especially among the peasantry, a much esteemed liquor is produced, called *poteen*. And although revenue officials are very numerous, the source from which it is obtained is very seldom discovered. This liquor is made from malted grain. Poteen is a low-proof alcoholic stimulant of a highly intoxicating nature, and is of Irish origin. It has never been successfully imitated. All sorts of contrivances are employed by these Irish peasants for distilling purposes.

While some use a regular still, others manage to obtain the *wee drop*, by means of pots or kettles.

A large three-legged iron pot, A (See Diagram No. 4) intended for boiling potatoes, is utilized. This serves the purpose of the still proper. A close fitting, cone-shaped tin cover B, with a small opening at the

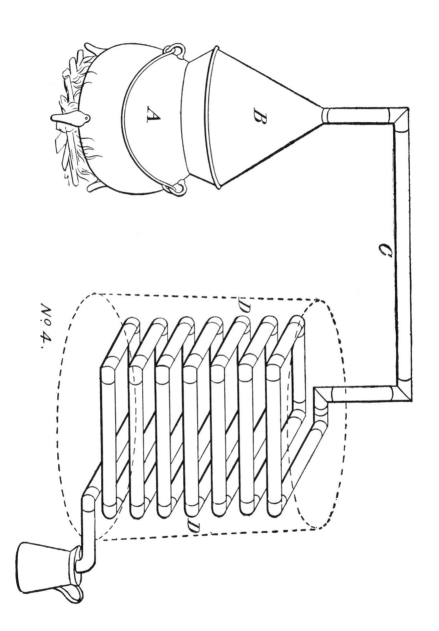

top, is connected with a long tube C of the same material. This tube sometimes leads through a running brook, the water of which serves to condense the vapor as it rises from the pot. Where there are no brooks, the same tin pipe is used in square coils D, fitted in a wash tub or barrels, (indicated by the dotted lines), which is filled with water. The fermented liquor is first put in the pot, the cover fitted on, the seams well closed, the tube which serves as a worm adjusted, a turf fire started, and the operation of distilling proceeds slowly. When all of the fermented liquor has been distilled, it undergoes a second distillation, the result is Poteen.

THE FARMER'S STILL.

The farmers in many parts of New England and elsewhere, find it more advantageous to convert their fruit into spirits than to dispose of them, which in many localities, it would not be possible to do, owing to the lack of transportation facilities.

The evasion of the Internal Revenue law is practised to a great extent. Kitchen utensils, such as large wash boilers, pot-ash kettles, as well as those intended for boiling maple sap, are brought into requisition. Tin, or galvanized iron pipe, serves for a worm.

In this rude manner, the fermented juice of apples, pears, peaches, grapes, currants and other fruits, are converted into spirituous liquors, such as apple jack, cherry brandy, peach brandy, etc.

A very ingenious substitute for a still was quite recently discovered in full operation in a steam sawmill. It was constructed in the following manner:

A strong ale hogshead was placed in a horizontal position with its bung upwards, a two-inch iron pipe was screwed into the bung hole ; a two-inch cock inserted in the head of the cask at the lower edge ; a half-inch iron pipe passed through one of the staves and connected with the steam boiler. The pipe from the bung was joined to a coil of pipe of the same dimensions, placed in a molasses hogshead, which stood upright, the upper head having been removed ; the extreme lower end of the coil extended through the lower portion of the stave. Live steam was used for heating the liquor. Fermented molasses constituted the charge ; the result was rum.

Enough has been said on this subject to convey a general idea of the arts and artifices employed by what are known as "moonshiners." We now turn our attention to the legitimate still and its auxiliary appliances.

THE ORDINARY COPPER STILL.

The ordinary still, such as is used in regular distilleries, consists of a copper boiling kettle, known as the still proper, and a spiral copper tube, graduating in size, from top to bottom.

The kettle (See Diagram No. 5) is built very shallow, with a concave bottom, and convex upper surface, called the "Breast." The top is somewhat broader than the bottom.

From the center of the Breast (A), a pipe connection (B) is made to extend to the upper portion of the tubing, called the "worm." G is the opening on the breast of the still in which the tubing (B) is inserted.

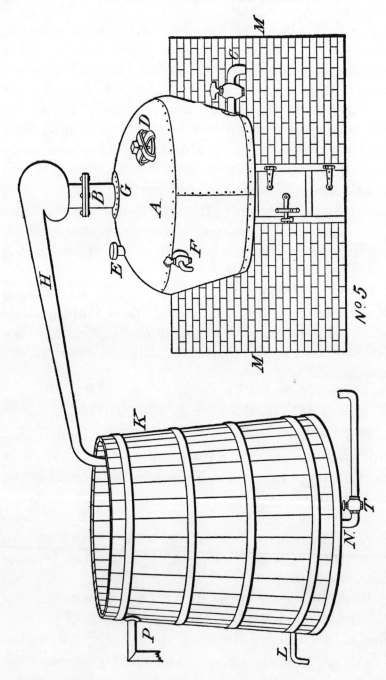

Nº 5.

The direct connecting tubing H is employed only when no other connections are used, such as the Doubler, the Column, or the Condenser known as the Goose, all of which will be explained hereafter.

The still is set in brick work with a fire box underneath, and a flue around the sides ; unless it be intended to heat by steam, in which case the still rests on a flat surface.

A large cock C is inserted at the side on a level with the bottom of the still. This is the discharge cock, and serves to empty the still of its contents after having run off the charge.

On the surface of the still (if a large one) is man hole D ; and near this, the charge hole E, which is a two-inch opening covered with a screw cap, to be removed or adjusted, as occasion may require.

At the side of the still, and at a distance of three-quarters of the height from the bottom, is a half-inch try cock F, and serves as an indicator in charging.

This concludes the general outlines or rudimentary description of the still.

THE WORM.

The worm is that portion of the apparatus through which all distilling operations are completed, and is of the utmost importance to the distiller ; it being the only part of the whole system capable of condensing the alcoholic vapors into liquid.

No matter how complicated the still works may be, whether consisting of one or more doublers, or column, the worm in every case forms the terminus.

There are other contrivances which are sometimes

N⁰ 6

employed as substitutes for the worm, but none so reliable. The following is the manner of constructing and adjusting a worm. (See Diagram No. 6). A copper pipe one hundred and fifty feet in length and graduating in size from four inches in diameter at one end, down to one and a half inches at the other, is bent so as to form from twelve to fifteen circles or spiral coils, all of which must be uniform in circumference, outside measurement, and separated one from the other about four inches. (See Diagram No. 6). These coils are held in position by short pieces of one-inch pipe soldered between them about three feet apart.

Heavy strap iron braces, reaching from the upper coil to the bottom one, are then bolted together in pairs, one inside and the other outside of the circles. Usually four pairs of these are used.

The lower ends of these braces rest on the bottom of the worm tub (See K, Diagram No. 5), when placed in position, and are secured to it by bolts running through the bottom of the tub, by this means the worm is held firm and secure.

In placing the worm in the tub, the lower coil should be eight inches above the bottom of the tub, with the small end projecting through the stave (See L, Diagram No. 5) into a square copper box, the bottom of which is supplied with a three-way cock.

The dimensions of this box are twelve inches by twelve in depth and breadth, and eighteen in length. In the centre of the worm tub and six inches above the bottom is a false bottom extending from the centre to the inner edge of the lower coil of the worm.

This serves to spread the cold water as it enters

into the tub by means of a two-inch iron pipe (See N, Diagram No. 5) at the centre of the bottom.

Six inches above the upper surface of the worm is a tin (or galvanized iron) pipe P three inches in diameter to carry off the overflow water while running a charge. The two-inch iron pipe which enters at the bottom is carried along the bottom to the outer edge where it ascends upward to the bottom of the reservoir tub, from whence it obtains its supply of water to cool the worm.

At a distance within convenient reach is a stop cock, which is used to regulate the flow of water, or shut it off when not needed. The water used for this purpose, should be at a temperature of sixty degrees Fahrenheit. When this can not be obtained, add ice to it, as much depends on cooling the worm in order to obtain a satisfactory result.

TO SET THE STILL.

When placed in its proper position, the still must be lower than any of its connections, in order to facilitate the management of the operation.

First of all, build the foundation upon which the still is to rest. This should be two feet in height with fire-box and ash-pit.

Place the still in position.

Build up the brick work (See M, Diagram No. 5), around the sides, up to the try-cock F, leaving a circular flue around the sides.

Set up the tub containing the worm K, in such a manner that the tail of the worm L may be two feet from the floor.

Connect the centre opening of the breast of the still with the upper portion of the worm by means of a copper pipe H made tapering from 6 to 4 inches in diameter.

The still is then ready for use.

Now for the tributaries, which include the Feed Tub and the Reservoir Tub. The first of these is placed in such a way that its contents can be drawn into the still by means of a hose.

The Reservoir Tub should be placed on the floor above, or what is still better, on the roof.

In most cases the goose and worm tubs are placed outside of the building.

This large tub serves as a water reservoir. It is from this that the worm tub obtains its supply. When placed in position, a two-inch iron pipe is run from its side, near the bottom, and carried to the outside centre of the bottom of the worm tub N, where it connects with a two-inch cock T, which penetrates the bottom and allows the water to flow in when running a charge, or shuts off the water flow when not in use. About four inches below the top of each of these two tubs is a four-inch galvanized iron pipe P to carry off the overflow of water.

The water used for cooling the worm is usually obtained from a well on the premises and pumped into the reservoir, or from a brook or spring on some adjacent hill and carried by means of a wooden or iron conduit to the reservoir tub. In a room below the still, (in some cases on the same floor), the receiving tub, the low-wine tub, and the reception-tub for the feints are located.

This completes the ordinary distillery, with the exception of the mash tub, fermenting tubs, etc., a description of which will be found elsewhere.

By carefully observing the following directions, any person possessed of a reasonable amount of intelligence and the least particle of ingenuity, can in a short time master the art, not only of constructing, but of operating any distillery for no matter what purpose it may be intended.

DIRECTIONS FOR ERECTING A DISTILLERY.

Directions for constructing a still of medium capacity. For Whiskey, Brandy, Rum, or Gin.

Height of still from the floor to shoulder. . 3 feet.

Breadth of concave bottom . . . . 42 inches.

Breadth of surface . . . . 5 feet.

Rise of breast from shoulder to centre . . . . 1 foot.

Opening in centre . . . . 6 inches.

Man hole . . . . 12 by 16 inches.

Charge hole with screw cap . . . . 2½ inches.

Length of worm (See Diagram No. 6) . . . 150 feet.

Diameter of upper section of worm . . . . 4 inches.

Diameter of lower section . . . . 1½ inches.

Height of worm tub . . . . 9 feet.

Breadth of worm tub . . . . 7 feet.

Discharge cock . . . . 2 inches.

Try cock . . . . ½ inch.

Breadth of worm coil, outside measure. 54 inches.

RUNNING A CHARGE.

When about to charge a still be sure that the discharge cock at the bottom is securely closed, then open the try cock on the side, remove the cap from over the charge hole, screw the hose on the cock at the side of the charge tub, lead the other end to and insert it into the charge hole on the breast of the still.

Open the cock at the charge tub and allow the liquor to run into the still until it begins to trickle from the try cock ; then close it, remove the hose, screw on the cap, and the still is charged.

Start the fire as soon as the liquor begins to run into the still and regulate it in such a manner that it may be drawn if necessary.

Keep a close watch on the apparatus to prevent it from running foul. When the liquor in the still becomes heated to the temperature at which alcohol boils, if the heat be *too* great it will cause not only the vapors to rise but the liquid itself. The volume arising being greater in bulk than the capacity of the worm to carry it off, owing to its tapering form, the apparatus becomes choked up or foul, and in many cases the bottom of the still is blown out and the contents lost.

This calamity can be avoided by adhering strictly to the directions as herein prescribed.

As soon as the surface of the still becomes heated, sound the connecting pipe between it and the worm with an iron-wire rod ; if it emits a hollow sound, it is an indication that all is right ; if on the contrary, a dull sound is produced by sounding, then the still is running foul.

In this case no time should be lost in drawing or covering the fire with ashes, clay, or sand, and deluging the surface of the still with cold water until the apparatus is clear again ; then start the fire again and heat very gradually until the liquor begins to flow from the tail of the worm. The first substance that rises and passes through the worm is a very offensive gas. This being excessively volatile does not condense in the worm but escapes into the air. As soon as this gas appears, the water supply must be turned on to the worm tub, and regulated so that the liquor may flow at the temperature of sixty degrees Fahrenheit. The first that comes over is highly impregnated with ether and fusel oil.

This first run is low wines, and should be received in a separate tub.

As the charge progresses the liquor becomes much sweeter and increases in proof, and, when it is made from grain, it is called whiskey. If from grape juice, brandy.

As soon as the sweet liquor is run off, which will be indicated by the sudden rise in the temperature, and a fall in the degree of proof, the remainder of the charge must also be run into a separate tub.

When it has been ascertained that all of the alcoholic substance has been obtained, the still is emptied, and charged again and run off as before. This is repeated until a sufficient quantity of sweet liquor has been obtained to compose a charge. It is then distilled over and over again, until the desired proof is obtained.

THE DOUBLER.

This appendage to the still is intended to double the alcoholic strength of the distilled liquor, and by this means to dispense with a second or third distillation. The action of the Doubler is to check the too rapid evaporation of water, by condensing and returning the condensed portion back into the still while allowing the vaporised alcohol to pass by and enter the worm. This is done in the following manner : Build a stout two headed tub, of one and a half inch staves, and two-inch top and bottom. (See A, Diagram No. 7).

Length of staves four feet.

Breadth of tub, forty-two inches at the top by forty-six at the bottom.

Cut two four-inch holes B, C, in the upper surface ; fit a four-inch collar flange to each. Insert a one-inch brass cock E in the side of the tub on a level with the bottom, and another D eight inches above it. Run a two-inch pipe F through the bottom of the tub midway between the centre and the stave. Let this project eight inches inside the tub, so that the top may be on a level with the upper side-cock. The lower end of this pipe is brazed to a collar flange, by means of which it may be connected with the still.

Run a four-inch copper pipe G through one of the collar flanges B ; let the lower end descend to within three inches of the bottom of the tub and the upper end project twelve inches outward, and brazed

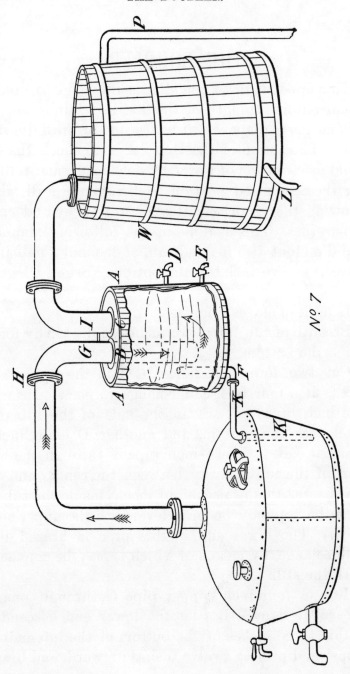

Nº 7

to a collar flange H so that it may be connected with the breast of the still. The other four-inch opening C connects by a four-inch pipe I with the worm contained in the worm-tub W.

The Doubler is placed midway between the still and the worm, its bottom being somewhat higher than the surface of the still, and the four-inch inlet turned towards it. In this position the inlet G is connected with the centre of the breast of the still, and the outlet I, which is the open four-inch flange, is joined to the worm. The two-inch pipe K called the return, passes through the breast of the still near the edge and is carried downwards inside the still to within two inches of the bottom, and the apparatus is ready for use.

When about to run a charge, fill the Doubler up to the side cock D with water. When heat is applied to the still, and the liquor which it contains vaporizes, it passes through the connecting pipe G from the still into the Doubler ; here it meets a resisting force, in the shape of five inches of water, through which it must pass or condense.

The first portion condenses and returns to the still through the two-inch return pipe K.

As the water in the Doubler becomes heated to the degree at which alcohol boils, the alcoholic vapors pass through it, and are as it were filtered, leaving the heavier bodies behind to be returned into the still in a liquid form..

It will thus be seen that although it may take a little longer to run a charge, the product must be of a greater alcoholic strength.

DISTILLATION OF LIQUORS.

BRANDY.

Brandy. This well known stimulant is the direct product of fermented grape juice, and is obtained only by distillation. The quality and quantity obtained depend on the nature of the grapes employed. The American grapes, as a rule, contain much less saccharine matter than the French, hence the wines are weaker, and produce a less quantity of brandy ; 100 gallons of ordinary grape juice should produce when distilled 25 gallons of brandy. The method for preparing and fermenting the grape juice is given on page 22. Distill in the same manner as described under the head of " *Running a Charge.*" (See page 37.)

CIDER BRANDY.

This is also known as apple jack, or cider spirits. It is made by first grinding the ápples into pulp, then expressing the juice. This is fermented, in the same manner as grape juice (See page 22) ; when the fermentation is complete it is distilled in a copper still and worm by the same method as employed for brandy.

BRANDY FROM BERRIES AND FRUITS.

Nearly all berries are capable of being converted, first into wine, then brandy. Strawberries, raspberries, huckleberries, currants, cherries, etc., are treated in the same manner as grapes.

WHISKEY.

Barley, rye, corn, wheat, and oats are employed in the production of whiskey, in various proportions, according to the method of the distiller ; such as barley and corn-meal, barley and rye-meal, barley and coarsely ground wheat, and in some cases malted oats, or malted rye. An excellent whiskey can be made by mixing

  5 bushels of barley-malt meal,
  10 bushels of corn-meal,
  10 bushels of ground wheat,
  450 gallons of water.

Mash and ferment according to directions, given on pages 13 and 19.

Run the fermented liquor through a still and doubler, or an ordinary still and worm.

HOLLAND GIN.

The original Dutch method.

Take 40 gallons of neutral spirits at proof,
  12 pounds juniper berries.

Put the spirits and berries together into an ordinary copper still, apply the heat very moderately and with great precaution, until the feints have come over (See *Running a Charge*, page 37), then increase the heat until the liquor flows regularly. Keep the fire uniform throughout the operation. The result will be Holland Gin.

WHEAT WHISKEY.

Take 50 bushels ground malt,
  250 bushels coarsely ground wheat,
  5,400 gallons water.

Heat the water until it indicates a temperature of 160 degrees Fahrenheit.

Run one-half of this water into the mash tub.

Sprinkle the meal into this water very slowly while stirring rapidly to prevent it from clodding.

When the meal has been thoroughly mixed with the water allow it to stand until it becomes quite clear. This will be in about two hours.

Then draw off 3,600 gallons of this liquor into cooling pans so that it may cool as rapidly as possible.

It will be found that when this liquor called " wort " is run into the cooling pans from the mash tub, it stands at 135 or 140 degrees temperature ; this must be reduced to 80 degrees, then run into the fermenting tub. This cooling process requires about five hours in winter or eight hours in summer. The specific gravity of the wort when drawn off into the fermenting tub should be 1·050, this will insure a good fermentation. Having drawn off 3,600 gallons from the mash tub, replace this with the same amount of water heated to 180 degrees temperature. Mix it thoroughly with the dregs and after standing until clear, run this off into another tub. This second drawing is not fermented ; it is used instead of water for mashing the second batch.

To the first drawing in the fermenting tub must be added two per cent. of fresh brewer's yeast to start the fermentation. (See *Fermentation*, page 19.) When complete, this substance is distilled through an ordinary still with doubler. The above is the method by which the best quality of wheat whiskey is produced.

RYE WHISKEY.

Take   90 bushels malted Rye,

　　　190 bushels Rye not malted,

　　　　　these may be coarsely ground or crushed.

　　5,200 gallons of water.

Heat the water to 155 degrees temperature.   Or, if it is more convenient, heat one-half at a time.   When thus heated, allow one-half, that is to say, twenty-six hundred gallons to run into the mash tub.

Sprinkle the meal into this water very slowly while constantly stirring to prevent the mixture from becoming lumpy.

When well mixed let it stand fifteen minutes, then stir again for five minutes ; repeat this four times, then allow the mixture to settle and when clear draw off 1,750 gallons into the cooling pans.   These pans should be broad and shallow enough to contain the liquor without exceeding the depth of a few inches.

Heat the next water to 180 degrees and run thirteen hundred gallons on the substance remaining in the mash tub, while constantly stirring as before.   When clear, which will take probably an hour, run off one thousand gallons of this liquor into the cooling pans.

Heat the balance of the water up to 190 degrees and repeat the operation of agitating and stirring.

After standing one hour draw this from the dregs into another tub to be employed for the next mashing, instead of the same quantity of water.

The first and second drawing when cooled down to 80 degrees are run into the fermenting tub, and when fermentation is complete (See page 19) are distilled. (See *Running a Charge,* page 37.)

Some distillers ferment and distill only the first drawing, while others mix the three together and ferment. In many instances where the proper facilities for malting are lacking, barley-malt is used instead of malted rye.

In this case the proportions are one bushel barley-malt to six bushels rye-meal, and eighteen gallons of water to the bushel of grain.

CORN WHISKEY.

There is in all probability more corn consumed in the production of whiskey than any other grain. There are a great many methods employed in converting the substance of this grain into spirits.

A percentage of barley-malt, be it large or small, is usually mixed in with corn-meal. This may vary from one bushel of malt to twelve of corn meal, up to seven of corn to five of malt. The steeping of the grain, in mashing, differs according to the theoretical ideas of the distiller. This accounts for some whiskeys being much superior to others, when produced from the same substance.

The flavor and quality of whiskey depend principally on the manner employed to extract the substance of the grain, (what is termed mashing). The longer it is boiled after steeping, the more fatty matter, and the more acid will be extracted, this fat forms fusel oil, the acid reverts into poisonous gases. These are changes which take place during the process of fermentation.

The proper manner of producing good corn whiskey is with the following ingredients and proportions :—

Use five bushels of coarse corn-meal to one bushel ground malt, and eighteen gallons of water to the bushel of mixed grain.

Boil one-half of the water, then mix it with the same quantity of cold water. This should bring it to 155 degrees temperature.

Draw one-half of this into the mash tub, and while stirring, sprinkle the meal into the water until it becomes well mixed and the substance resembles thin gruel; repeat this stirring at intervals of fifteen minutes for the space of two hours, then allow it to settle.

When clear, draw off two-thirds into broad shallow pans, in order that it may cool rapidly. This will prevent the formation of acetic acid. When cooled down to 80 degrees, run it into a fermenting tub, and add to it two per cent. of fresh brewer's yeast.

When fermentation is about to stop, (See page 20) run it into the still, and conduct the operation according to the directions under the head of *Running a Charge*. Having drawn off two-thirds of the liquor from the mash, heat one-half of what remains to a temperature of 180 degrees. Run this into the mash tub with the first; mix thoroughly as in the former case; allow it to repose 45 minutes, then run it off into the cooling pans. Repeat this the third time with the balance of the water heated to 190 degrees; allow it to stand one hour, and draw this off into a separate tub.

Mix the second and third drawings together, and use this mixture in the place of water in the next mashing.

GIN.

The method here given is employed in New York, Buffalo, and Cleveland, Ohio.

Take 112 pounds barley-malt,
　　228 pounds rye-meal,
　　96 gallons water.

Heat the water to 162 degrees Fahrenheit.

Sprinkle the malt in this water together with the rye-meal, stirring the substance briskly while doing this.

Let this infusion remain for three hours; then bring the strength of the mash down to 1.047 specific gravity, this is done by adding cold water. This will bring the temperature down to 80 degrees Fahrenheit.

Run this liquor off clear from the dregs into a fermenting tub, and add half-a-gallon of brewer's yeast. This must be allowed to ferment for forty-eight hours only.

The clear liquor is then run into the still and undergoes the process of distillation; the low wines being kept separate from the sweet liquor.

It will be readily understood that forty-eight hours of fermentation have not been sufficient to extract all of the substance from the grain. A quantity of saccharine matter still remains.

The low wines which have been obtained are mixed with the dregs and sediment and all run into the still together and distilled.

When the liquor has been secured, the first and second distillates are mixed together with fifteen pounds of bruised juniper berries and a double handfull of hops, this substance then undergoes another distillation.

The gin produced by this process is fully equal to any in the country and far superior to that made from grain spirits.

If found too expensive, this system can be modified to suit the occasion. If found to be too high flavored, reduce the proportion of juniper berries or vice versa. For instruction in the manner of conducting the distilling operation, see *Running a Charge*.

RUM.

The solution from which Rum is distilled consists of the juice as well as parts of the sugar cane, and in many instances the residue of sugar boiling establishments, principally in the West Indies, Jamaica, Barbadoes, St. Croix, etc. The production of rum differs from that of whiskey, inasmuch as no brewer's yeast is employed.

When a sufficient quantity of refuse is gathered together it is put into a tub, saturated with water and well stirred ; it is then allowed to stand until fermentation sets in, which in the first instance is very slow ; that is at the commencement of the sugar boiling season. The reason of this is, that they have no yeast to start the first batch. After this however there is no further trouble, as the yeast gathered from the first serves to excite the next batch.

When the fermentation is complete (See page 21) the liquor is distilled in the same manner as brandy, whiskey, or gin.

When first made, rum has a peculiarly disagreeable

flavor which wears off as the liquor grows older. When there is a good demand for rum, and the sugar crop is bountiful, rum is made from molasses, or molasses and sugar, as well as from the refuse. That which is made from the scummings and other waste matter alone is called *Sugar-spirit*.

ARRACK (OR ARRAC).

This is a species of Rum produced in the East Indies. The ingredients used for the purpose are rice and the juice of the cocoa or palm tree. The process is very peculiar especially in obtaining the material.

The operator provides himself with a number of earthen pots with small necks. With these fastened to his girdle or belt, he climbs up the tall trunk of the cocoa tree ; having reached the boughs, he cuts off certain small buds with a knife and applies one of the bottles or pots to the wound and fastens it with a cord, and so on until all of the pots have been disposed of. These pots receive the juice as it flows from the wounded parts of the tree. This operation is usually performed in the evening, as the flow of juice is greater at night than in the day. In the morning the pots are taken down and the juice emptied into a large vessel or tub, where it under-goes fermentation ; after which it is distilled into low-proof liquor.

A quantity of ground rice is then macerated and fermented in the same manner ; this, when distilled, produces another quality of low-proof alcoholic sub-stance.

These two are then mixed together and are re-distilled, the product being Arrac. In other parts of India, the juice and seeds of the tree are all fermented with the rice and then distilled.

RECTIFYING.

This is also known as "Leaching," and consists of a system by which liquors are purified by filtration through ground charcoal.

The tub used for this purpose is called a Leach-tub. This is built of ash wood, the usual size being five feet in height by seven feet in breadth.

A perforated false bottom is fitted twelve inches above the regular one. This false bottom is made to rest on four cross bars; these in turn are supported by small upright posts.

The holes in this false bottom are one-quarter of an inch in diameter, and one inch apart. A coarse linen cloth is stretched over these apertures, and the seam well caulked with the same material.

Twenty-five bushels of coarsely ground charcoal is packed over this cloth; this is covered over with loose bagging of any description, and over the bagging some loose boards, and a sufficient quantity of stone to keep them in position when submerged.

The liquor to be rectified is run into this tub, and as it filters through the charcoal, the fusel oil is held by the charcoal while the alcoholic substance passes through. Thus the liquor becomes purified,

The rectified liquor is drawn from this tub by means of a brass cock placed at the side of the tub on a level with the bottom. In order to facilitate drawing off this liquor, a quarter-inch tube is adjusted to the inner side of the tub, and extends from the top, downward and through the false bottom. This allows the air to enter as the liquor is withdrawn, and to escape while the space between the real and false bottom is being filled.

High wines, a new whiskey, when purified in this manner is known as pure spirits, and used by compounders for adulterating purposes. If re-distilled through a column, it is called French high-proof spirits.

There is also another method by which liquors are purified without the use of charcoal or leach tubs, known as the chemical process. (See *Alcohol Refining.*)

THE COLUMN.

The column forms the principal portion of the alcohol still. It acts in the same manner upon vaporised bodies as the doubler, with twelve times its capacity ; that is to say, whereas the doubler condenses once, the column condenses twelve times during one operation, thereby increasing the alcoholic strength of the liquor at each condensation.

The column, as seen in diagram No. 8, is composed of twelve sections, each of which is a cylinder, made of sheet copper, eighteen inches in height, and thirty-six in breadth, with a flat bottom in the centre of which is a four-inch hole.

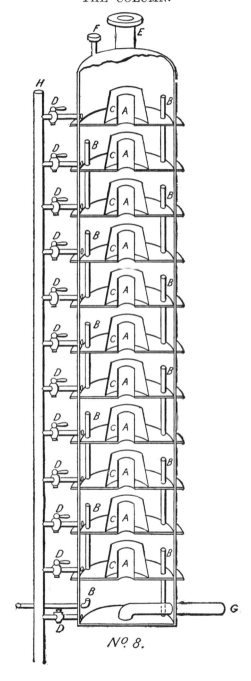

N? 8.

Two copper pipes pass through this bottom ; one a four-inch, A, through the centre ; the other a two-inch, B, near the edge. The four-inch pipe projects eight inches upwards, and sets exactly upon the four-inch hole and flush with the bottom plate, to which it is firmly soldered.

The two-inch pipe or "plunger" is carried upwards seven inches, and extends sixteen inches through the bottom of the cylinder, thus projecting downwards into the next cylinder below, and reaching to within two inches of the bottom of it; this is also firmly soldered into the bottom plate. A copper pan called a "cap," C, twelve inches across the bottom, and sixteen inches wide at the rim, is placed inverted directly over the four-inch pipe, and two inches above it, with the lower edge reaching down to within two inches of the bottom plate.

This pan is held in position by three legs, soldered first to the sides of the pan, then to the bottom plate. A straight one-inch brass cock, D, extends outward from the side of the cylinder and on a level with the bottom plate.

The upper and lower edges of the cylinder are turned outward, forming a flange, by which means the sections can be connected.

This completes one section of the column.

The bottom and top sections differ from the others, inasmuch that the top one is covered over, a four-inch exit pipe, E, being fitted in the center of its dome, and a cap-hole, F, near the edge of the cover.

The two-inch pipe, B, of the lowest section, instead of passing through the bottom, is made to pass through the side near the bottom plate, in which there is no four-inch aperture; the inlet pipe, G, enters through the side, and opens near the bottom of this section.

The first, or lowest section, is placed upon a scaffolding, two feet higher than the breast of the still.

The connecting pipe, G, from the still enters this at the side, three inches above the bottom plate and discharges two inches above the bottom.

The two-inch pipe, B, from this bottom section enters the breast of the still, and is carried down inside the still to within two inches of the bottom. (See K, Diagram No. 7.)

The second section is then placed on the top of the first, the third on the second, and so on to the top one. In placing these sections one over the other the side cocks, D, must be in line, and fronting the still.

These cocks, D, which are used in charging the column, are connected with a one-inch copper pipe, H, placed in a vertical position, and extending from the upper section to one foot below the lowest one.

The upper end of this pipe is closed; the bottom soldered to a one-inch brass cock. This pipe serves to charge the column, and also to empty it of its contents when necessary. It will be seen that, when these cocks, D, are all closed, excepting the one at the bottom, and water is let in to the column from the cap hole, F, on the upper section, as soon as the water reaches to the height of the uppermost plunger B which rises seven inches, it will overflow and pass through this plunger, to the next section. This is con-

tinued until the overflow of water reaches the bottom
section, when it will flow from the bottom plunger, B,
which has been left open for that purpose. The
column is then, what is called "charged," each section
containing seven inches of water on its bottom.

As the sides of the pans, C, which are placed over
the four-inch pipes, A, reach to within two inches of
the bottom plates, it will be seen that they are submerged to the depth of five inches.

When the vapors as they ascend and pass through
the four-inch pipe, G, come in contact with the
bottom of the lowest inverted pan, they cannot
escape upwards, but they spread and are carried
down its sides, forced to pass through the water and
escape outside the pans to the upper part of the
cylinder, and enter the next pan above, or condense
into liquid.

The heavy bodies, such as water and oils, are condensed; this increases the bulk of water, and causes
it to overflow into the two-inch pipe, B, which carries
it back to the cylinder below it, and so on to the
bottom cylinder, whence it passes to the still.

The alcoholic vapor being much more volatile than
water, passes through the water, and ascends around
the exterior of the pan, concentrating in the upper
portion of each cylinder, and entering into the next
section above, where it meets a like obstruction, and
is again purified of its watery element, and so on to
the top section where a pipe fitted to E connects it
with the goose (See diagram No. 9) in which it is
again subjected to a like treatment, but in a different
manner.

THE GOOSE.

That portion of the alcohol apparatus called the goose, is the last through which the vapors pass on their way to the worm, and is in itself a powerful condenser. (See Diagram No. 9.)

It consists of twenty-four joints, A, of four-inch copper pipe, each forty-two inches in length, and while in an upright position six inches apart, are joined together by means of semi-circular elbows, B, at top and bottom, thus forming a continuous conduit ; one end of which is connected with the top of the column, and the other with the worm.

A two-inch pipe, C, connects the lower portion of each bend with a pipe, D, in such a manner as to carry off any liquid that may be condensed at the lower curves of the goose. This pipe D is closed at the end nearest to the worm, while the other end passes to, and enters the upper chamber of the column at the side, then downward to within one inch of the bottom plate. This condenser or "goose," when complete should stand in a tub or tank in the form of two acute angles, "or conduplicate" so that the part which connects with the column may be nearest to it, while the last section will be nearest the worm.

When placed in the goose-tub, there should be a space of one foot between the inner edge of the tub and the copper work.

Seven-eighths of the goose must be submerged in water when in operation, one-eighth remains above the surface.

Near the upper edge of the tub is a three-inch tin pipe to carry off the surplus water ; this is called the overflow pipe. The supply of water is obtained by means of a two-inch iron pipe which enters the tub in the centre of the bottom. A circular covering is placed directly over this inlet and about two inches above it, extending from the centre about eighteen inches ; this causes the water to spread as it enters, instead of rising to, or near the surface as would be the case were it not checked in its ascent.

Some of the large alcohol distillers use a double goose in the same tub. The vapor enters both at the same time by means of a Y joint and exits to the worm in the same manner.

DISTILLATION OF ALCOHOL.

This branch of the business has given rise to more scientific research than all other branches combined, the principal aim being to find a means of producing alcohol in its purity, free from water or other elementary bodies. How far this investigation has been successful will be demonstrated as we proceed.

The high wines from which alcohol is produced are subjected to another and far more complete distillation than that by which they were obtained. For this purpose, a complicated apparatus is used.

This consists of a still, a column, a condenser (called the goose), and the worm, each of which have been previously described.

By this system we now obtain alcohol at 190 degrees of proof or 95 per cent. pure alcohol. The still

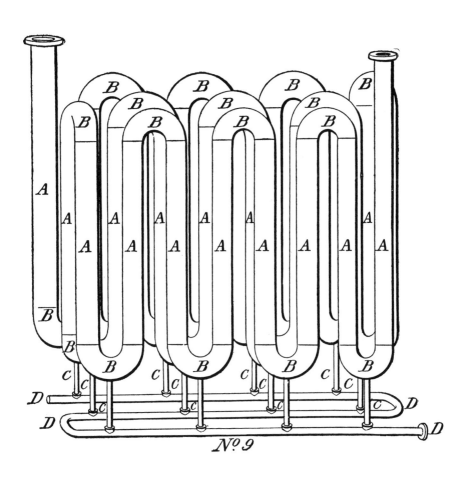

N.º 9

may be of wood, iron, or copper, and heated by steam.

A six-inch copper pipe connects the lower chamber of the column to the centre of the surface of the still.

The *Column* is divided into twelve equal sections, called chambers. These chambers are so constructed that as the alcoholic vapors pass from the still into the lower chamber, the heavy bodies condense and are returned to the still; the alcoholic portion being lighter, passes through, and ascends to the second chamber, and thus from one chamber to another, each section in turn rejecting the condensed portion and returning it to the chamber next below and finally back into the still.

The alcoholic vapors having reached the upper chamber, pass through this and are conveyed through a connecting pipe to the goose, where they are again condensed; the heavy bodies returning to the column, and the lightest portion of the vaporized substance proceeding on its way until it reaches the worm, where it in turn is condensed into liquid, and this liquid is alcohol. (See *Column* and *Goose*, pages 52 and 57.)

In connecting the different portions of the alcohol apparatus, place the still on the lower floor of the building, the worm tub on the next above, the goose tub one floor above the worm tub, and the water tank (or reservoir) on the roof.

These tubs are usually built on scaffolding, outside of the building. The receiving tubs are placed on the same floor with the still. The column runs up through two floors, its upper section being two feet below the level of the bottom of the goose tub, while the bottom plate of the column is two feet above the surface of the still.

The liquor which is to be converted into alcohol must first be reduced to 95 proof, what is called 10 per cent. below proof. It is an established fact that when the column of water predominates over that of spirits, it facilitates the separation of the two bodies. The still is charged in the same manner as the whiskey still (see *Running a Charge*), after which the column is charged, the goose and worm tubs are filled with water, steam is turned on to the still, and in the goose tub. The water in the goose tub is heated by means of a one-inch steam pipe from the steam boiler. When heated to the temperature at which alcohol boils, the steam is shut off. This heating is done in order to facilitate the running of the charge.

When the liquor within the still becomes heated to the boiling point of alcohol, the vapors ascend, and pass into the lower section of the column, causing a loud rumbling, and crackling noise. This is caused by the hot vapors passing through the cold water with which every section of the column is charged.

As the noise ceases a low rumbling is continued, until the hot vapor passes from the first to the second section when the rumbling is heard again as before. This is repeated at every section until having reached the upper chamber the vaporised body passes from it into the goose, the rumbling noise then ceases and is followed by a low monotonous sound which continues to the end of the operation.

As soon as it is found that the vapor has reached the last section of the goose, cold water must be let into the goose tub from the bottom, very gradually at first, and increased as occasion may require. The water which serves to cool the worm, is also let in from the bottom as soon as the liquor commences to flow from the tail of the worm.

Regulating the flow of water in these two tubs to correspond with the pressure of the ascending vapors requires the utmost caution. It may be said that the whole art of alcohol producing is concentrated in this. The water in the goose tub must be kept up to the boiling point of alcohol; if heated beyond this point it will cease to act as a condenser, the watery vapor will pass together with the alcohol and thus reduce the proof. If on the other hand the water is too cold, the alcoholic vapors condense and return to the column, this action cools the column and prevents the alcoholic vapors from rising and the whole operation is suspended. When the liquor commences to flow from the tail of the worm, it will be seen that the first fifty or seventy-five gallons will be below the standard, this must be run into the low-wine tub.

Supposing the charge to be twenty-five barrels.

As soon as the liquor indicates 92 sp. grav. on the stem of the hydrometer, it must be allowed to run into the alcohol tub.

The water in the warm tub is to be kept at a temperature of 60 degrees Fahrenheit. It will be observed that when the proof of the running liquor indicates a fall in alcoholic strength, and a rise of temperature, it shows that the spirits have all been extracted from the still, and what has not been secured is contained in and is passing through the different sections of the column. This is ascertained by drawing some of the liquor from the try cock, (See F, Diagram No. 5) pouring it on the breast of the still and touching it with a lighted match ; if there be any spirits remaining in the substance, it will burn, if not, the steam should be shut off, as well as the flow of water in the tubs, and the still emptied and charged anew.

This will save much time in conducting the second operation. Not only this, but will also keep the apparatus in a proper condition.

If the operation is allowed to continue to the end, the heat must be increased, the water in the goose tub shut off, while the supply into the worm tub is increased.

When the low wines have all passed over, a mixture of water and fusel oil follows ; this continues until nothing but clear distilled water is obtained. This part of the operation is called running off the column, or cleaning up, and occupies about three hours.

This is the ordinary method of producing alcohol. Such as is used for artificial purposes.

When pure inodorous alcohol is required the liquor from which it is obtained is subjected to another operation called *Leaching,* which is one system, or *Refining,* which is another. (See *Rectifying,* also *Refining.*)

ALCOHOL REFINING.

What is called Refining differs from Rectifying. In the latter case ground charcoal is employed to absorb the oils and ethers; while in the former, the oils and ethers are completely destroyed and the alcohol obtained free and inodorous.

In order to be more explicit on this subject it will be necessary to refer to the first production of alcohol and examine into the chemical laws which govern the formation and separation of different bodies.

There are two powerful agencies which act on all substances by opposite methods, these are heat and cold.

Heat is the great antagonist of atomic affinity ; it transforms solid bodies into liquids, vaporises the liquid and converts it into gases.

Cold on the other hand causes the atoms to combine, gases are condensed to liquids, and liquids to solid matter.

When bodies become separated by the agency of heat, they form other combinations, which differ from the first; as has been proven in the transformation of starch into sugar, and sugar into alcohol. These new unions take place only when the different components are within the sphere of each other's attraction.

When whiskey or high wines is heated the affinity of the component parts of which it is composed, that is,—alcohol, water, fusel oil and ether,—is destroyed. There being no other bodies present with which they can unite, they remain free ; as shown during the process of distillation, ether being the most volatile escapes first and is lost in the air ; alcohol vaporises next, followed by fusel oil ; while water, being the heaviest body, comes over last.

As the alcohol vaporises, a portion of the oil and of the water is carried over with it. This does not form a chemical compound, but a mixture, as each body can be afterwards separated and obtained pure.

To this cause is attributable the difficulty of obtaining alcohol free from impurities by the ordinary means of re-distillation. With the new system, however, this obstacle has been removed, years of research and practical experience having resulted in the successful introduction of this improved method of which the author of this book is the inventor. The manner of operating is somewhat similar to the usual method by which all alcohol is distilled. The same apparatus is used, the same amount of heat is employed and the same system of condensation. The only exception being the introduction of chemicals into the liquor at the exact moment when the affinity of the constituents is destroyed by heat.

For this purpose a wooden tub, V, Diagram No. 10, is placed a few feet above the still, usually on the floor above it. A one-and-a-half-inch copper pipe connects the bottom of this tub to the center of the surface of the still, with a stop cock, W, directly over the still and another, Z, at the tub connection. This tub is called the chemical tub.

When all is ready and the still is charged, which in this case must be with liquor containing fifty-five per cent. of water, then proceed in the following manner :

While the liquor in the still is heating, dissolve in a tub with hot water twenty pounds of pearl ash, and in another tub the same amount of soda. When properly diluted pour both of these solutions into the chemical tub, V.

This proportion is intended for a charge of twenty-five barrels.

When the liquor in the still becomes heated to the temperature at which ether vaporises, which is 96 degrees Fahrenheit, (this being the time when the elements begin to separate), allow the contents of the chemical tub to flow gradually into the still by first opening the upper cock, Z, to permit the pipe to fill, then the lower one, W, so that the solution may pass very slowly into the still.

As soon as this alkaline mixture, which forms a powerful base, comes in contact with the fat of which fusel oil is composed, it acts upon it at once by expelling all less powerful bases, and uniting with the fat, forming soap, or properly speaking a solution of soap and water. This solution spreads all over the surface of the liquor as a scum. This new union not only destroys the fusel oil but prevents the heavy bodies from vaporising, while the alcohol being so much lighter rises and is carried over.

When condensed, it is found to be a perfectly pure spirit, free from taste or smell.

The advantages gained by this method are very plainly evident ; it absorbs the fusel oil at the moment when the temperature is most favorable for its complete separation from other components; it

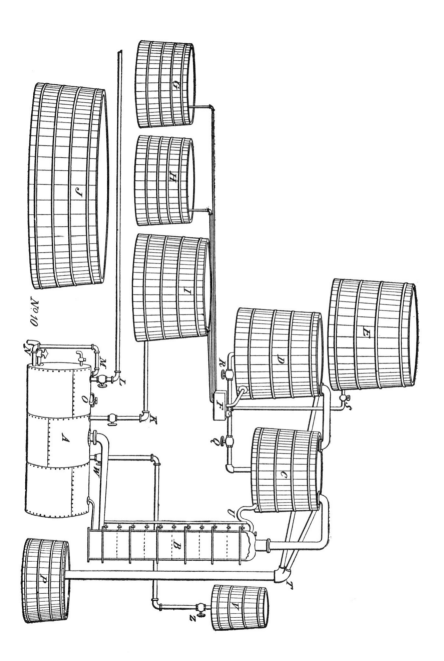

saves the time, labor and consequent expense of subsequent rectification, during which operation it is
necessarily exposed to the action of the atmosphere.

DISTILLATION OF VOLATILE OILS.

These oils are obtained by distillation and when dissolved in alcohol, their solutions are called Essences.

These essences are employed for flavoring liquors,
confectionery, etc. Oils of this description are met
with in all kinds of plants, in the leaves, the bark, the
roots, and in the flowers.

In some instances the same plant may furnish different oils, such as the orange tree, which furnishes
one from its leaves, another from its flower, and a
third from the rind of its fruit.

These oils are obtained in the following manner :

The substance from which they are to be extracted is allowed to steep in cold water twenty-four
hours, after which it is run into a still and heat
applied. The water vaporises and passes over into
the worm, and is condensed, passing from the outlet
in liquid form.

It will be found, however, that the oil has been carried over with it, and can be seen floating on the surface. The supernatant oil is drawn off and put up in
bottles with ground glass stoppers, and is ready for
use.

The separation of the oil from the water may be
effected by the use of a glass syphon. It may also
be done by an arrangement called a Florentine

Receiver. A glass vessel, narrow at the top, so as to present only a small surface for evaporation, is fitted with an escape tube close to the bottom ; this tube is bent upwards to a height a little lower than the mouth of the vessel. As soon as the distillate, dropping into the vessel, has reached *a*, the level of the upper bend in the escape tube, the water flows over at *b*, into a suitable vessel, and continues to escape as fast as the supernatant oil accumulates on the surface, until the water has all been thus displaced

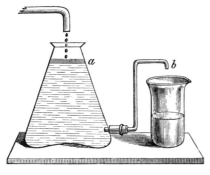

and separated. The illustration will make this easily understood.

For oil heavier than water, the escape tube is fitted at *a*, allowing the water to flow off as the oil below displaces the supernatant water.

Some substances yield their volatile oil very readily, and therefore require little or no maceration previous to being distilled; in this case the substance is introduced into the still with an equal bulk, or perhaps more, of water. This plan may avoid any loss of oil which might occur by exposure during the period of maceration.

The water-bath may be made to yield a higher degree of heat, if necessary, by adding a proper proportion of salt to the water in the outer vessel or bath.

The still employed for volatile oils, etc., will be easily understood by Diagram No. 11. The ordinary worm is replaced by a condensing jacket, C.

A is the still.

J the charge hole.

I the exhaust cock.

B an alembic passing through a hollow jacket, C.

H is a barrel, situated above the level of the jacket, containing ice-water.

G the stop-cock regulating the flow of water into F.

F a funnel, to receive the water, set into the upper side of the lower end of the jacket.

D an escape pipe, leading to a waste tub, by which the water passes off as fast as it enters at F.

E a glass jar to receive the distillate.

The principal oils which are obtained in this manner are :

Oil of juniper berries.

Oil of orange-peel.

Oil of Bergamot.

Oil of roses (known also as otto of roses).

Oil of peppermint.

Oil of wintergreen.

APPLE OIL.

This oil is a chemical product of which fusel oil forms the basis.

Take 2 parts fusel oil.

4 parts acetate of potash.

2 parts sulphuric acid.

Distill by means of a water-bath still. The product will be a volatile liquid with a strong and very agreeable odor. For " Water-Bath Still " see page 73.

Add to this ten times its volume of 95 per cent. alcohol. Bottle at once using ground glass stoppers.

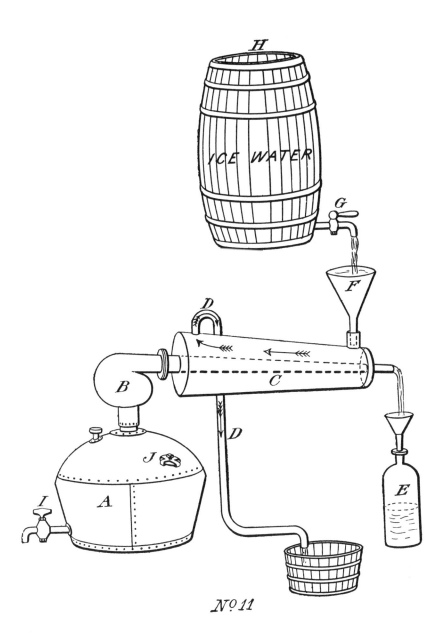

ICE WATER

H

G

F

D

B

C

D

J

I

A

E

Nº 11

PINE APPLE OIL (CALLED BUTYRIC ETHER).

Take 2 parts alcohol.

2 parts butyric acid.

1 part sulphuric acid.

Mix all together and dissolve in twelve times its weight of alcohol.

EXTRACTS

In the production as well as in the compounding of liquors, more or less flavoring matter is employed. These flavors consist principally of Extracts, Essences and Tinctures.

Extracts are obtained by different methods.

First: by expressing the juice from the plant.

Second: by soaking in cold water and then pressing.

Third : by boiling.

These processes are technically called Pressing, Infusion and Decoction.

The liquor thus obtained is filtered, then evaporated, leaving a pulpy, pasty mass. This is Extract.

This substance can be kept for years. One ounce of this extract contains as much active matter as several pounds of the vegetable substance from which it is extacted.

As an illustration let us take a quantity of liquorice root, say ten pounds.

Pour on to this seven gallons of boiling water.

Allow this to remain a few days, then press out the liquor and filter it. It will be found to be clear and transparent. Let it evaporate in an open vessel.

A dull black substance resembling pitch will remain. This is the extract, and is known as Spanish liquorice.

It will be seen that evaporation in the open air has not only changed the color but also the taste.

This proves that the only true method of obtaining extracts is by evaporating in a closed vessel, such as the still. In this manner the properties of all vegetable matter can be extracted pure and unchanged for flavoring or for imparting an aroma to wines or liquors.

Some substances yield their extractive matter readily by simple infusion ; others require infusion, boiling water, and sometimes decoction ; others, again, yield only sparingly in water, and require alcohol, diluted or pure as circumstances demand. Percolation is also sometimes employed. The substance is first ground to powder, and then packed in a cylindrical or a funnel-shaped vessel, having an outlet at bottom. The liquid is poured gradually into the upper part, filters through the powder and drops from the bottom exit into an appropriate receiver, and afterwards evaporated.

The best method to be adopted depends entirely upon the substance to be operated upon.

THE WATER-BATH STILL.

The still used for distilling cordials is of a peculiar design. The boiler consists of two parts somewhat similar to a carpenter's glue-pot. The part, C, diagram No. 12, which is intended to contain the substance to be distilled is shaped in such a manner that it may fit inside of a larger kettle, A, leaving a sufficient space between the two to hold as much water as would be contained in the smaller one when filled to two-thirds of its capacity. These stills are made to be connected, or disconnected at the pleasure of the operator.

The material to be distilled is put in the inside kettle ; water is let in to the outer one until it reaches to three-quarters the height from the bottom which is indicated by a small cock, G, placed there for the purpose.

The connection is made to the worm by a loose joint of pipe, J, bent in the proper shape ; brown paper saturated with raw flour-paste is wound around the seams, then the heat is applied. The process of distilling is conducted in the same manner as for whiskey or brandy.

The water in the outer compartment of these stills can be heated by steam, either with or without a coil of pipe ; what is known as live steam answers all ordinary purposes. Where steam can not be had a fire underneath, whether of wood, coal, coke or fagots is all that is required. The usual capacity of stills of this description is about forty to sixty gallons. Compounders and manufacturers of essential oils, perfumes, essences, and extracts use much smaller ones, ranging from two to ten gallons capacity.

For experimental purposes a glass apparatus known as a retort is generally employed ; these can be procured at any wholesale drug and chemical establishment.

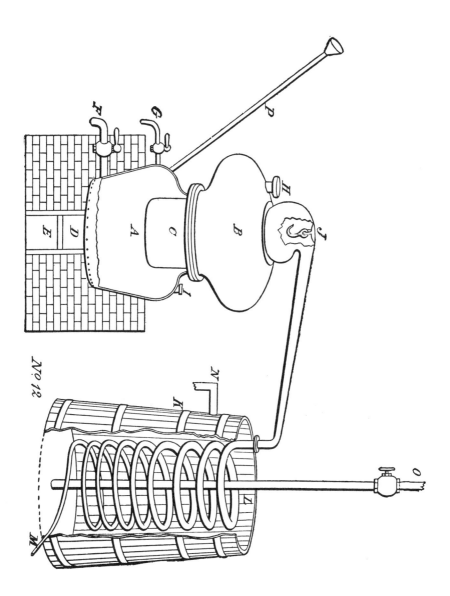

No. 12

Some prefer to have these small stills made of heavy tin. Any tinsmith can construct one at a very small cost. A worm, L, for a ten-gallon still should be thirty feet in length, graduating from $2\frac{1}{2}$ inches in diameter at the top down to $\frac{3}{4}$ of an inch at the bottom, forming a coil of ten circles, and placed in a tub, K, four feet in height by two and a half in breadth; this must be firmly secured. (See *Worm*.)

ESSENCES.

ESSENCE OF GIN.

The following is the English method of preparing it. Use for this purpose the finest spirits.

　　　Take　1　gallon spirits 20 above proof,
　　　　　　2　ounces caraway seeds,
　　　　　　$2\frac{1}{2}$ ounces fennel seeds,
　　　　　　1　pound juniper berries.

Grind the seeds, and bruise the berries; stir them thoroughly into the alcohol and place this mixture in a still, adding one quart of soft water.

From this, distill just *one* gallon and no more. What remains in the still is of no use, as it is of a very disagreeable odor.

This essence should be put into bottles with ground glass stoppers, until required for use. The best method is to let the seeds and berries macerate and digest in the spirits five days before distilling.

ANOTHER METHOD.

Take 10 pounds juniper berries,
 1 pound fennel seeds,
 1 pound caraway seeds,
 $\frac{1}{2}$ pound lemon peel,
 $\frac{1}{4}$ pound orris root,
 $\frac{1}{4}$ pound orange peel,
 2 ounces cardamom seeds,
 3 ounces hops.

Put these ingredients in an earthen jar, with spirits enough at 120 proof to cover them.

Allow them to remain six days; then add two gallons of water, and distill slowly to within a half a gallon of the quantity placed in the still.

RED RATAFIA.

This Liqueur, as it is called, is very popular in many parts of Europe, and also in the United States. It is far superior to the cordials in general use. The manner of preparing it is this:

Take 24 pounds ripe red cherries,
 4 pounds ripe black cherries,
 3 pounds ripe raspberries,
 3 pounds ripe strawberries.

Bruise the cherries and berries together.

When well bruised, allow them to remain in that condition twelve hours, then press out the juice, measure it, and to every quart add half a pound of brown sugar.

When the sugar has been properly dissolved in the juice, filter through a coarse linen bag.

When filtered, add to it three-quarters of a gallon of fine rectified spirits. This concludes the first operation.

The second is as follows :

> Take 4 ounces cinnamon,
> 1 ounce mace,
> 2 drachms cloves.

Bruise them together in a mortar.

When well bruised, pour one gallon of good clean proof-spirits over them, then add a half gallon of soft water.

The water-bath still is then prepared and the spices together with the liquor in which they are steeping are put into it.

Next apply a gentle heat to the still and draw off one gallon by distillation. This distillate is called spiced spirit and is generally kept on hand in all places where cordials are manufactured.

Add of this spiced spirit a sufficient quantity to the material obtained by the first process to make it agreeable to the palate, which will be about one quart. This is the only true way of preparing this liqueur.

There is another method adopted by some of the manufacturers, which is to allow the juice of the fruit, after being pressed, to ferment several days, to increase the vinosity of the liquor, but in doing this the rich fruity flavor is greatly diminished.

When prepared according to the manner first stated and it is desirable to strengthen the liquor, it is done by adding more spirits, and thus still retain the fruity flavor.

Another system is also employed in the distillation

of the spices. The spices are tied up in a linen bag, and suspended by a hook in the still, thus allowing the vapor of the spirits to pass through them while ascending. In this case, more spirits is required to obtain the same result.

All fine French liqueurs are prepared in this manner.

ANISETTE.

This celebrated liqueur is compounded and prepared to a very large extent in France and Italy. It is made in the following manner:

Take 20 pounds green anise,
3 pounds star anise,
1 pound coriander seed.

FIRST:—Wash the green anise in soft water; grind the coriander; then put the whole in 40 gallons of 95 per cent. alcohol; add to this four gallons of water, and run this all together into a water bath still.

Apply a good heat, and distill thirty-five gallons.

Then pour ten gallons of water into the still; apply more heat, and distill again, run off six gallons, and mix it with the first run.

Try the alcoholic strength of the liquor; and reduce it with soft water to 80 per cent.

SECOND:—Make a syrup of six hundred pounds of sugar, dissolved in thirty gallons of water; when boiled three minutes, filter through flannel, and when cold, add this to the distilled liquor.

Mix it well, then filter through felt filters, and the anisette is ready for bottling.

The operation of distilling French liqueurs, such as anisette, absinthe, curaçoa, maraschino, etc., should be performed in a regular cordial still, fitted with a water bath.

ABSINTHE SUISSE.

Absinthe is a product of Switzerland. It is well known on both continents as a powerful stimulant and is highly esteemed by the French. The greater portion used in this country is imported in bottles direct from the country whence it originated. The manner of producing this liqueur was for many years kept a profound secret, being handed down from father to son for generations. It is now prepared to a certain extent in this country by French cordial manufacturers, who have succeeded in producing an *Absinthe* which when ripened by age, is in every way equal to that which is imported, and, in fact can not be distinguished from it.

Take 20 pounds long absinthe (wormwood),
    24 pounds small absinthe   "
    33 pounds green anise seed,
    33 pounds long fennel,
    33 pounds star anise,
     4 pounds coriander seeds,
    10 pieces hyssop.

Put all of these ingredients into 125 gallons of fine spirits at 190 proof.

Allow this to remain twenty days, stirring once every day, at the expiration of which time the whole substance is put into a cordial still, together with fifteen gallons of water, and distilled.

The distilling in this case requires great precaution in its management. The heat must be kept uniform throughout the whole operation, so that the liquor will flow very regularly ; not too fast, as that would render the product bitter ; not too slowly, as it would be milky.

The exact heat required in this instance can only be learned by experience ; the operator must be guided by the flavor and aroma of the running liquor, during the process.

When the charge is nearly run off, a fact which is ascertained by comparing the amount distilled, with that which has been put in the still, keep a strict watch for the feints, or low wines ; this is indicated by the running stream diminishing in size and the liquor becoming milky.

At this stage of the operation, the receiver must be changed, and the feints run off separately, as they are not suitable for mixing with the clear running. The quality of the product will depend in a great measure on the proper observation of this latter precaution.

If quantity is more an object than quality, or if a second quality is desired, as soon as the feints appear, add more water to the dregs in the still and distill again ; this second drawing may be mixed with the first or used as second class goods.

When the distillation is completed, the next thing is to color the liquor.

For this purpose take as follows :

> 5   pounds mint leaves,
> 2½ pounds melissa leaves,
> 3½ pounds hyssop,
> 5   pounds small absinthe,
> 5   pounds liquorice root (cut).
> 1½ pounds citron peel.

Put these ingredients in the liquor which has been distilled, and allow the whole to remain until the desired color is obtained ; then draw it off into another cask and reduce the alcoholic strength to 120 proof, or in other words, 60 per cent. and it is ready for bottling.

MARASCHINO.

Take 70 pounds of peach pits, put them into 35 gallons of fine 95 per cent. alcohol.

Allow them to digest four weeks ; then pour this substance, pits and all, into a cordial still arranged with a water bath.

Add to this, when in the still, the tincture of 5 pounds of peach flowers.

Distill slowly to prevent the oil from rising, which would impart a bad taste.

As soon as the feints begin to show, (see *Absinthe*), change the receiver ; stop the operation by withdrawing the fire ; add 10 gallons of water to what remains in the still ; continue the distillation, reserving the last run to be worked off on the next charge.

Reduce the first to 30 above proof, (65 per cent.)

then add 90 gallons of syrup, the same as prepared for Ratafia. (See page 77.)

CURACOA.

This liqueur, when properly made, is one of the most popular in use. It is in great demand by connoisseurs both here and in Europe.

For this purpose, use only the finest quality of high-proof alcohol.

> 25 gallons alcohol (refined),
> 35 pounds green orange peel,
> 50 pounds yellow orange peel,
> 4 gallons soft water.

Allow the ingredients to infuse ten days, stirring twice each day, after which it is put in a water-bath still, and distilled very slowly.

As soon as twenty gallons have been drawn off, stop the operation; change the receiver; then add ten gallons of water to the material remaining in the still, and continue the distillation until all is run off.

The second run is kept apart and used for preparing a subsequent charge.

The first liquor drawn from the still is the ordinary curaçoa, before being sweetened, which is done in the same manner as maraschino.

DOUBLE CURACOA DE HOLLANDE.

This is prepared by redistilling the first drawing of the still, mixed with five gallons of water. The coloring is made and put in afterwards; and is composed of the extract of Brazil wood, campeachy wood and yellow wood.

ON BLENDING AND COMPOUNDING.

The term *blending*, as used in the wine and liquor trade, denotes the mixing of two or more substances, of the same nature, such as strong and weak wines, high flavored brandies with those that are deficient in fragrance, old and new whiskeys, etc.

When wines and liquors are reduced by adding water, and a fictitious alcoholic strength imparted to the mixture, it is called *adulteration*. If drugs and chemicals are employed in connection with alcohol and water, the product is known as a *compound*. These three operations constitute the art of the compounder. This branch of the business is very extensive and has reached such perfection that experts are often deceived.

The successful results in this as well as in other branches of the business depend in a great measure on the ability and resources of the operator.

The art of artificially imparting qualities to new wines and liquors, identical with those produced by age, as well as the reproduction of chemical compounds, requires not only tact and skill but a certain amount of practical experience, and a thorough knowledge of the composition of alcoholic products.

In preparing the ingredients which are to be employed in the production of artificial wines or liquors the first care is to see that they are properly dissolved, otherwise the union will be imperfect. The improper treatment of one ingredient will sometimes destroy the whole batch ; or one substance may neutralize the effect of another. In either case the operation will prove unsuccessful.

It is well known that oil and water will not unite. Oils, fats and some acids form new compounds when mixed with alkalies ; some substances will dissolve in alcohol or ether ; many ingredients which are not soluble in alcohol are readily dissolved in water.

Roots, herbs and spices when employed, are steeped from seven to fifteen days in spirits and used in the form of tinctures.

It is evident therefore that whatever ingredient is used, unless it is treated according to its constitutional requirements, it will either neutralize the effects, or cause the destruction, of some other body, thus possibly producing an obnoxious scent that will diffuse itself throughout the whole mass.

COMPOSITION OF WINES AND LIQUORS.

Analytical experiments have from time to time been made by expert chemists with a view of ascertaining the nature and qualities of the constituent bodies of which wines and liquors are composed.

The result of these experiments show that, with the exception of the flavoring principle, the component parts are nearly, if not quite, identical, and consist of alcohol, water, sugar, tannin, tartaric acid, acetic acid, fusel oil, glycerine, ammonia and a volatile ether.

When these ingredients are reunited, in the same proportion as they existed before being separated, it will be found that instead of a reproduction of the wine or liquor as it was before undergoing the analytical operation, a disagreeable repugnant, unpalatable mixture will be the result.

This proves that chemical bodies after having been once set free can not be successfully reunited. Certain changes take place at each sucessive operation, not in the *separating* of the component bodies but in their *reuniting*. No two liquids can be mixed without creating more or less friction. Friction generates heat ; heat expands and separates the particles. These particles lose their identity in uniting with others and thus form new compounds, as will be seen under the head of *Alcohol Refining*.

PERCENTAGE OF ALCOHOL IN WINES AND LIQUORS.

It has been found by distillation that wines and liquors contain alcohol in the following proportion, which however, is subject to variation, especially in wines, some vintages being richer in saccharine substance than others, thereby producing more alcohol.

100 gal. French brandy	contain 53 gal. Alcohol.
100 " Jamaica rum	" 53 " "
100 " Holland gin	" 53 " "
100 " Scotch whiskey	" 53 " "
100 " Irish whiskey	" 52 " "
100 " American whiskey	" 46 " "
100 " Port wine	" 20 " "
100 " Claret wine	" 17 " "
100 " Burgundy port	" 16 " "
100 " Gooseberry wine	" 11 " "

100 gal. Rhine wine	contain 12 gal. Alcohol.
100 " Cider	" 9 " "
100 " White wine (Barrac)	" 10 " "
100 " Porter	" 7 " "
100 " Ale (old)	" 7 " "
100 " Ale (new)	" 4 " "
100 " Lager beer	" 3 " "

One brand, only, of each of these wines and liquors was experimented upon. Some brewers produce much stronger ales and beer than others.

The same may be said of distillers. Rochelle brandies are generally higher in proof than those of cognac, while American whiskeys are supposed to be 100 proof. Cider is also variable owing to the quality of the fruit, as well as the manner of production.

HINTS FOR COMPOUNDERS.

In compounding wines, liquors or bitters, there are many obstacles which present themselves.

The spirits may be but poorly rectified, in which case no satisfactory result can be obtained.

If the oils, acids or alkalies, are not properly dissolved they will fail to unite, and in many instances counteract or neutralize the effects of each other. When tinctures are employed in improper proportions, they act in nearly the same manner.

TO REMOVE A BAD TASTE.

If a bad taste has been imparted to whiskey through the indiscriminate use of essential oils or tinctures, it can be partially if not wholly removed by adding to every forty gallons of the liquor one pound of dried apples and half a pound of dried peaches.

Cut them up fine and allow them to steep in the liquor ten days; then filter the liquor. A bad taste is removed from brandy by treating it in the same manner, using one pound of ordinary raisins and half a pound Malaga raisins, instead of the apples and peaches.

FLAVORINGS FOR COMPOUNDED LIQUORS.

FOR BRANDY.

A quarter of an ounce of oil of cognac dissolved in sixteen ounces 95 per cent. alcohol will flavor forty gallons of pure spirits.

FOR GIN.

A half of an ounce of oil of juniper berries will flavor forty gallons of spirits.

FOR FRUITY FLAVOR.

Five pounds of prunes, bruised in a mortar with five pounds of raisins, and steeped eight days in five gallons of spirits, will impart a fruity flavor to two hundred gallons of liquor.

FOR AN ASTRINGENT FLAVOR.

Five pounds of black tea boiled thirty minutes in six gallons of water, then pressed to extract the substance and mixed with five gallons of proof spirits, will supply an astringent for five barrels of liquor.

FOR AN ARTIFICIAL BEAD.

Sweet oil and sulphuric acid both produce a fictitious bead on liquor.

FOR THE BED-BUG FLAVOR.

What is called the bed-bug flavor is produced by a few drops of strong ammonia in a barrel of liquor.

SIMPLE FLAVORINGS.

Compounders usually make use of the following ingredients when an acidity is required :   Cream of tartar, acetic acid, acetic ether, tartaric acid, citric acid, etc., where in fact a small portion of strong vinegar would answer the same purpose.

Tannin, catechu, and kino are employed to impart an astringent, where black tea answers a better purpose.

If liquors require sweetening use plain white syrup.

If they require coloring use burnt sugar, which is called " caramel" by the French ; and " coloring" by liquor dealers.

Oil of neroli, anise oil, orris-root, ambergris, musk, civit and vanilla beans, are frequently employed for flavoring liquors. These as well as many other ingredients used are of no use whatever in compounding liquors. The flavorings which have been given under their respective headings will be found quite as good, and sometimes far superior.

FORMATION OF ALCOHOL.

The formation of alcohol is a subject which has received the utmost consideration. Careful and diligent research as well as practical experience teaches us that this substance does not exist in plants. It is not formed in the air. Neither is it an artificial product.

Upon further investigation we find that it is a chemical compound, the result of putrefaction.

Alcohol constitutes the intoxicating portion of wines, beer and liquors.

These liquors all undergo the process of fermentation; this destructive action decomposes the sugar which is contained in the solution, and as the component particles become disunited, alcohol is formed. Of this we have abundant proof as will be shown in the succeeding remarks.

As alcohol owes its origin to sugar, the latter, or a large portion of it, is also a chemical product. Grape sugar is formed by the action of the elements, principally from the starch contained in the grain. This chemical transformation is the first which takes place when the seed begins to sprout, and is called *germination*.

This is explained in the following manner: It is well known that the germ of every seed is surrounded by a mass of starchy matter to protect and preserve it.

If however this seed becomes damp, and the temperature is favorable, it absorbs water and oxygen from the air; this produces heat, which causes carbonic acid to be thrown off. The starchy matter undergoes a change and forms a new substance called *diastase.* This new substance is capable of exciting fermentation.

Germination is produced on a large scale by the process of malting.

CONVERSION OF STARCH INTO GRAPE SUGAR.

Starch as it exists in plants is not soluble in cold water until it is acted upon by the power of heat.

If a quantity of starch from plants or seeds be placed in an oven heated to a temperature of 300 degrees Fahrenheit, it becomes soluble in water and changes into gum. This gum, when boiled in a weak solution of sulphuric acid, becomes a limpid fluid called *dextrine.*

When the boiling is continued a few hours, the acid is removed by neutralizing with chalk, the liquid is filtered and evaporated, and it will be found that a mass of solid grape sugar will remain, which will exceed in weight the starch from which it was produced.

This operation then has produced the same result as germination or malting, in converting starch into sugar.

CONVERSION OF SUGAR INTO ALCOHOL,

The second chemical action is the transformation of the sugar into alcohol, which is known as fermentation, and consists of three continuous actions.

The first is the *vinous,* the second, the *acetic,* and third and last, *putrefaction.*

The vinous fermentation decomposes the sugar and alcohol is formed; it then stops, and the alcoholic portion is extracted. If this is not done, fermentation commences again.

This second fermentation destroys the alcohol, and vinegar is formed.

If the operation is allowed to continue, the vinegar is also destroyed by putrefaction.

This illustrates the difference in products resulting from the transformation and decomposition of the same substance. First, germination or malting destroys the starch contained in the grain and produces grape sugar ; this in turn decomposes and forms carbonic acid and alcohol.

The alcohol, that is to say the hydrogen which it contains, unites with the oxygen of the air, the alcohol is lost and a substance called *aldehyde* is formed. This in turn is changed into acetic acid, diluted with water. This solution is vinegar.

It may be readily understood that alcohol when formed and obtained by distillation is heavily charged with impurities. While the sugar is undergoing the process of decomposition, a portion of it forms a fatty substance, while another portion is transformed into a gaseous body called ether.

The fatty part is known as *fusel oil ;* the ether is due to the part of the sugar which, after having passed through the vinous fermentation, has continued on its destructive course until reaching the stage where putrefaction sets in, and the substance, being decomposed, reverts back to the elements.

These impurities being lighter than water vaporise

with the alcohol and pass over with it ; the oil and a portion of the ether are condensed in the worm, while the lighter body, which is known by its offensive odor, being set free, escapes in the air. This accounts for the harshness of all newly distilled liquors.

It is from this oil and ether that they obtain their respective flavors. This harshness wears off in course of time ; the oil becomes purified and partly absorbed in the wood, while the ether escapes through its pores.

When new whiskey or high wines are intended for the manufacture of fine alcohol suitable for compounding spirituous liquors or wines, these impurities must be removed, which is done by another process, called rectifying or leaching. (See *Leaching*.) There is also another method employed which is called refining with chemicals. (See *Alcohol Refining*.)

ALCOHOL WITHOUT DISTILLATION.

It has been stated that alcohol is obtained only by distillation. This is true as far as the practical method is concerned; nevertheless, to prove beyond a doubt that alcohol exists in wine or beer before distillation, and is not formed but only eliminated, during the latter process ; and furthermore that it is not contained in unfermented wine or beer ; but is the direct product of fermentation, the following experiment will furnish convincing proof.

Take a small quantity of wine, cider, or beer, being satisfied that no spirits of any kind have been mixed with it ; pour this liquor into a glass tube, say a half an inch in diameter, and two feet long ; fill this half full of the liquor ; then drop into this tube small pieces of carbonate of potash, (this must be perfectly dry), the carbonate will soak up all the water ; continue this by degrees, and when the water is all taken up, the pure alcohol will gradually rise to the surface, and stand in a distinct stratum over the other contents.

This method is very frequently adopted for testing the alcoholic strength of wines, cider, beer or ales.

When it is necessary to know the exact quantity contained in any liquor, a graduated tube is used for the purpose.

The tube is somewhat similar to that of a thermometer, only a good deal larger ; the length of the tube is divided into one hundred equal parts ; this is done on a strip of white paper which is pasted on the outside of the tube. By this means the exact quantity or percentage of alcohol contained in any liquor can be ascertained.

ABSOLUTE ALCOHOL.

In the preceding part of this work it has been explained how alcohol is obtained from sugar ; how it is formed ; how it is separated from the wine or beer, how purified, etc. This purification is practically speaking an incomplete distillation ; or if the distillation be complete, the condensation is incomplete, since it is well known that alcohol vaporises easier than water, and its vapor is more difficult to condense than steam, and yet, all the water can not be separated from the spirits. In this manner, the alcohol retains a portion of water so firmly that it can neither be withdrawn from it by distillation, nor by cooling.

In order to procure it absolutely anhydrous, a body must be presented to it which has a greater affinity for water than the alcohol itself.

When such a body is presented it fixes upon the water so firmly that it cannot evaporate with the alcohol at the boiling point of the latter.

When it is desirable to obtain alcohol in such a shape, quick lime is used for the purpose. An ordinary glass retort with one ounce of quick lime, broken in small pieces, and one ounce of strong alcohol poured over it as soon as it is placed in the retort, is all that is required.

As soon as the two ingredients are placed in the glass retort, it is connected with the receiver, and is allowed to remain twenty-four hours.

During this time the lime gradually combines with the water, which the alcohol may contain ; this slacks the lime, and in doing so, loses its own identity, whereby the alcohol is left free, and can be distilled off by applying a gentle heat. This should be done by placing the receiver over a water-bath. The distillate will be found to be Absolute Alcohol.

ALCOHOLIC ETHER.

During the process of distilling high wines for the production of alcohol, the first body that comes over and passes through the worm is a gas or what may be properly called a stench. Its odor is remarkably offensive to the eyes and lungs. This gas instead of condensing escapes in the air.

It originates during the process of fermentation.

When the yeast, introduced in the unfermented liquor in order to induce fermentation, has passed the vinous action, it enters the acetic; and while the sugar is being converted into alcohol the yeast having passed both vinous and acetic stages, enters into the last destructive action (putrefaction), and by the time alcohol is formed, is totally decomposed. The volatile portion of this putrefied body being lighter than alcohol, expands when heat is applied, and is forced over by the alcoholic vapors.

FUSEL OIL.

Fusel oil is formed during the process of fermentation. It is the fatty portion of the grain. It forms an imperfect combination with other bodies, such as acids, ether, etc.

The peculiar flavors of all whiskeys are due to the presence of this oil. When extracted from the liquor, and purified, it forms the basis of other flavors such as apple oil, pear oil, etc.

MANUFACTURE OF VINEGAR.

Vinegar is a solution of water and acetic acid. This substance, like alcoholic spirits, is subject to impurities. As alcohol owes its origin to the decomposition of sugar, vinegar in like manner is obtained through the destruction of alcohol.

There are several methods by which vinegar is produced. There is however but one principle, which is the action of the air upon alcoholic substances.

When vinegar is made from wine, beer, or cider, the liquor is exposed to the air. The action of the elements produce a slow fermentation ; this fermentation decomposes the alcoholic portion of the liquor, wine, or beer, and acetic acid is formed.

When refuse vegetable matter is employed (as farmers often do), it is put into a barrel or hogshead, with eighteen or twenty times its bulk of water. The saccharine matter which it contains soon ferments and is converted into alcohol, and from alcohol into vinegar.

When, as is often the case, there is not a sufficient quantity of saccharine matter present, instead of fermenting, the whole mass turns to putrefaction.

The great bulk of vinegar which is employed in pickle and preserve establishments, is made from new whiskey, or high wines. The apparatus used for this purpose is called a "generator," and is constructed and operated in the following manner.

VINEGAR GENERATOR.

This consists of a tub, which may be large or small, built for the purpose. Say ten feet high, by four feet wide. It should be made of beach, maple, or ash wood. The tub, A, Diagram No. 13, stands on end, on a scaffold two feet from the floor.

Instead of the upper head, B, being placed at the top, it is fitted two feet below the upper end of the staves.

This head, or shelf as it may be called, is perforated with small holes, four inches apart. In these holes are placed straws or pack cord. Between these small holes there must be a number of half-inch holes into which glass tubes, C, are inserted. These tubes project upwards to near the top of the staves.

The sides of the tub from the shelf down to within two feet of the bottom is also perforated with numerous large holes. This tub is nearly filled with beach shavings which have previously been saturated with strong vinegar. The generator is now ready for use.

CONVERTING ALCOHOL TO VINEGAR.

To perform this operation, wine, beer, ale, porter, cider, whiskey, or alcohol may be employed.

When the two latter are used they must first be reduced to the consistency of wine or cider.

The substance to be converted into vinegar is poured in at the top of the tub to within one inch of the upper ends of the glass tubes, and as it filters through the shelf it is replaced by fresh liquor.

A

B

N.º 13

As the liquor filters through or between the straws or pack cord, it diffuses itself over the shavings, and forms a very thin liquid layer which presents to the air a surface many thousand times more extensive than was produced by any former method.

It is erroneous to suppose, as some do, that the shavings have anything to do with the formation of vinegar, except in supplying the necessary surface.

The object of perforating the tub on all sides is to secure a free circulation of air. This is indispensable. As the cold air enters through the holes in the sides of the tub it comes in contact with the alcohol which is diffused over the shavings. The alcohol absorbs a portion of the oxygen in the air; this generates heat, or slow combustion. The temperature within the tub therefore rises, the air becomes warmer and consequently lighter, which causes it to ascend and escape through the glass tubes. As it escapes, the cold air rushes in and thus the interior of the tub is continually supplied with fresh air.

In this process of manufacturing vinegar it is necessary before commencing the operation to saturate the interior of the tub as well as the shavings with strong vinegar and also to mix a little with the material to be employed.

VINEGAR BY THE QUICK METHOD.

For this purpose an ordinary still is employed. The grain is mashed and fermented in the same manner as for the production of whiskey. It is then run into the still,

As the vapors arise, instead of being conducted to the worm, and there condensed into liquid, they pass directly through a number of tubs filled with beach shavings. These tubs are so arranged that the first empties into the second, the second into the third and so on and finally comes out of the last one very strong vinegar.

The foregoing methods are intended for manufacturing purposes; vinegar intended for family, or hotel use is prepared in a different manner. Some choice vinegars are obtained by artificial flavoring, as is the case with what is called French vinegar.

FRENCH VINEGAR.

This is prepared in the following manner :

Take 1 ounce long pepper.

1 ounce ginger.

1 ounce pyrethra.

Bruise these, and put them into a saucepan over a rather brisk fire. Add one and a half gallon of white wine.

When it comes to a boil, remove it from the fire ; transfer it to a porcelain vessel, and let it stand in the sun, or over an oven, in fact, any warm place will answer.

As it cools, add more wine heated as before, about three quarts at a time ; transfer this into a wooden keg ; place the keg in a warm place, and as the liquor cools add more warm wine, three quarts at a time, until it amounts to ten gallons, then add to this three quarts of strong vinegar.

FRENCH VINEGAR POWDER.

For the use of travelers, tourists and explorers, who find it difficult in many countries to procure good vinegar, a powder is prepared in the following manner:

Wash half a pound of white tartar with warm water, then dry it thoroughly. Pulverize it as fine as possible. Soak the powder in good sharp vinegar and dry it again. Repeat this ten or twelve times. The drying process can be accomplished either in the sun or an open oven.

By this method a thoroughly impregnated vinegar powder is produced, so powerful that a few grains will convert water into vinegar in a moment.

The explanation of this process is that water evaporates much more readily than acetic acid.

By soaking the powder in vinegar and drying, the water evaporates and leaves the acid behind; this combines with the solid matter and becomes fixed. When the soaking is repeated, and again dried, more acetic acid is retained by the tartar. It will be readily understood therefore that the oftener the operation is repeated the stronger will be the powders.

DISTILLING VINEGAR.

Vinegar is sometimes distilled in order to strengthen it. This operation is the opposite of distilling liquors. Water is more volatile than acetic acid, and as the water evaporates by distillation the vinegar becomes stronger and is withdrawn from the bottom of the still richer in proportion to the amount of water extracted.

THE CONTINUOUS RECTIFIER.

This is a comparatively new French invention. It was first introduced, and is now in use at *La Maison Caille*, Paris, France, which is no doubt the most extensive rectifying works in that country, if not in the world.

This new system is so different from the American as well as the English methods, that it is with a somewhat reluctant feeling that I now for the first time attempt a comprehensible elucidation of this complicated French method for the production of fine deodorised alcohol. My reluctance is owing to the fact that my practical experience in the working of the apparatus has been rather limited; not sufficient in fact to warrant me in passing upon its merits, or imperfections.

This new system, it is claimed, possesses the following advantages :

FIRST : Economy in time and fuel.

SECOND : The double action by which fine alcohol is distilled in one part of the apparatus at the same time that the feints, or low wines, are being distilled off in the other part.

THIRD : In keeping the alcohol column sweet and clean by excluding low wines from its chambers.

FOURTH : The system of employing three-way cocks which act simultaneously by closing one outlet and opening another.

FIFTH : By utilizing the exhaust steam from one still to run off the low wines and feints in another.

CONSTRUCTION OF CONTINUOUS RECTIFIER.

Two boiling kettles or stills (A and AA, Diagram No. 16) built in the usual manner, are placed on a brick or stone floor, six feet apart. A stout platform is built in the rear of this intervening space upon which rests the column B, and an appropriate scaffolding to support the colonette C. The column is sixteen feet in height by forty-two inches in diameter, and is composed of eight sections, each section forming two chambers. The colonette is nine feet in height, by twenty-four inches broad, and is composed of six or eight chambers, each chamber forming one section.

Each of these sections is formed into a cylinder, with an out-turned rim extending two and a half inches, by which the different sections are secured when in position.

Each of the large sections contains a perforated copper plate, (N, Diagram No. 14) which is both rivetted and soldered in the centre of each, giving it the appearance of a huge strainer.

These plates are perforated with quarter inch holes, one and a half inch apart. The holes are punched in with an ordinary hand punch on a block of wood ; when the plates are hammered after punching, it leaves the holes three-sixteenths of an inch which is the proper size.

When the eight large cylinders are thus prepared, a bottom plate (F, Diagram No. 14), is riveted to one of them, and a dome covering is riveted to another. These two form the top and bottom of the column.

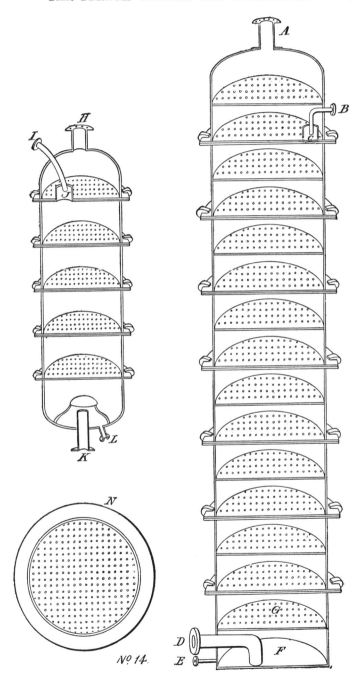

N⁰. 14.

Seven plates are then prepared which extend to the outer edge of the out-turned rims of the cylinders. These are also perforated in the same manner as the centre plates.

A five-inch copper pipe, D, is then inserted through the side of the cylinder containing the bottom plate. This pipe is bent downward and extends to within four inches of the bottom plate. A one-and-a-half-inch pipe E extends (six inches outward) from the side of the cylinder on a level with the bottom, both pipes being fitted with a brass collar-flange.

The column is then set up as follows : The section which is fitted with a bottom is placed on the platform with one of its two pipe connections facing each of the two stills; a loose perforated plate is placed over it, then an open section, and another loose perforated plate.

This is continued up to the last open section, the loose plate in this case being different from the rest. A copper basin, C, is soldered on to this plate mid-way between the outer edge and the centre.

This basin is six inches broad by six inches in height. A pipe, B, of one and a half inches diameter is passed through the side of the topmost section, one inch below its centre plate. This pipe is bent downward in such a manner that when the upper section is put in place, the pipe will reach to within one and a half inches of the basin. This is termed a "plunger."

The top, or domed section being in place, the colonette is built up in the same manner, and clamps adjusted. (The clamps are described further on.)

The pipe connections are then adjusted. Two large three-way cocks (D, and DD, Diagram No. 16) are placed, one over the centre of each still ; these two cocks are connected by means of a five-inch copper pipe, I, with a T joint, V, in the centre by which they both connect with the column, B.

From the opposite outlet of each cock another five-inch pipe (H, and, HH, respectively) connects the two to the bottom of the colonette, C. It will be seen that by opening these cocks on to the column it closes them on the colonette and by reversing the action they open on to the colonette and close on the column.

The return pipes from the column are connected by means of another three-way cock, d.

A one-and-a-half-inch pipe, W, leads from the bottom of the column to the centre of the intervening space between the two stills, and is connected to the three way cock, d. From this cock two pipes, J, J, diverge in opposite directions, and pass through the breast of each still, and are carried to within two inches of the surface of the steam coil which covers the bottom of the stills.

A one-inch three way cock, Y, serves to connect the colonette to the stills in like manner. In this instance the cock is adjusted to the bottom of the colonette, from which the two pipes, K, K, diverge, and are carried to, and through the breast of the two stills, to near the bottom.

These return pipes serve to convey the condensed liquid, as it accumulates, back into the stills.

The steam fitting comes next. As a general rule, the steam boiler is placed in some outbuilding, or in the cellar. A precaution which is intended to prevent the alcoholic vapors from coming in contact with the flames of the fire, when the furnace doors are open.

The steam for heating the stills is conveyed from the steam boiler, through a two-inch pipe, E, to a point directly over the nearest still, where it diverges into two one-inch pipes, through which it is supplied to the stills ; a steam globe valve, 6 and 7, being placed one on each still for the purpose of regulating the steam pressure, when the stills are in operation. These valves connect in the interior of each still with a one-inch copper pipe that leads to a coil of pipe of like dimensions, called the steam coil. This coil covers the whole surface of the bottom of each still. The inlet for the steam is at the centre of the coil, while the outlet is near the outer edge and passes through it twelve inches above the bottom of the still. It will be seen that by means of these valves, the steam can be supplied to one, or both, stills at the same time, or shut off, as may suit the convenience of the operator. The exhaust pipes in this system demand special attention. Iron pipe connections are made to the outlet of each coil. This piping, F, F, is carried upward to the height of the breast of the stills, where each pipe crosses over to the still opposite, passing through the breast, or surface, and connecting in the interior with the coil, at or near the place where the steam pipe connection is made. It will be observed by referring to the cut, that the exhaust piping is supplied with four one-inch globe valves, marked respectively, 1, 2, 3, 4. By closing 1 and 3, and opening 2 and 4, the exhaust passes off into a tub known as the exhaust tub, the contents of which serve to feed the steam boiler. By closing 1, 2 and 3, the exhaust passes from still, A, into and through the coil of still, AA, and escapes through 4. This will be more fully explained hereafter.

The dome of the column is connected with the goose, L, and the goose, L, with the worm, M, in the same manner as the American column, which has been fully described in a preceding part of this book.

The colonette however differs in its connections. Instead of a goose and worm, it connects from its dome to what the French term, *Le petit condenseur*, which acts in the double capacity of goose and worm.

A special description of which will be found under the head of "French Condenser."

THE CLAMPS.

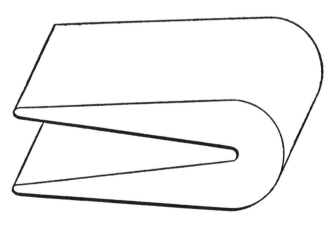

Nº 15

French distillers and rectifiers when constructing a column, or other works of that description, instead of employing large flat iron rings, together with screw bolts, in order to secure the different sections one over the other, use what are called Clamps (*see* cut). These possess a great advantage over the iron flange system. The time required in building up the column is lessened by more than half. In case of a leak, a light tap with a hammer on the two or three clamps where it occurs will stop it at once.

These clamps are forged by hand of what is known as horse-shoe iron.

DESCRIPTION OF DIAGRAM NO. 16.

A. AA. Two ordinary still kettles.

B. French column.

C. Colonette.

D. DD. d. Three three-way cocks.

E. Steam feed pipe.

F. F. Exhaust steam pipes.

G. Try cock, or side cock.

H. HH. Two vapor pipes to colonette.

I. Main connecting pipe for vapors.

J. J. Two return pipes from column.

K. K. Two return pipes from colonette.

L. Goose tub.

M. Worm tub.

N. Condenser tub.

O. Two discharge cocks.

P. Return pipe from goose to column.

Q. Air chamber.

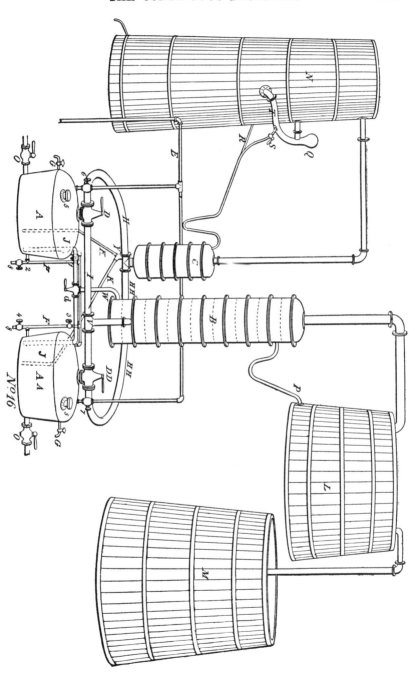

R. Return pipe from condenser to colonette.

S. Safety cock at foot of air chamber.

T. Connection between upper and lower condensers.

1, 2, 3, 4. Four globe exhaust valves.

5, 5. Two screw caps used when charging stills.

6, 7. Two steam globe valves.

8, 8. Two pipes leading to exhaust tub.

TO OPERATE THE CONTINUOUS RECTIFIER.

Fill the still, A, with the liquor which is to be converted into alcohol, until it commences to trickle from the side cock, G.

Close the cock, and remove the charge hose, screw on the charge cap, 5.

Turn on the steam gradually at 6. Close exhaust valves, 1, 2 and 3. Open 4.

Open valve, D, on to the colonette, C.

Open valve, DD, on to the column, B. This puts the apparatus in the first running order.

As soon as the liquor becomes heated to the boiling point of alcohol, the vapor rises and will pass through the colonette in about fifteen minutes. When this vapor reaches the condenser it is checked, condensed, and returned to the colonette, this continues an hour or more, when the liquor begins to flow from the outlet of the condenser.

As soon as this occurs, the water must be turned on at the bottom of the condenser tub. This must be done very gradually and regulated according to the run of the liquor. Should the volume of water be excessive, it will prevent the flow of the liquor. If it should be insufficient, the liquor will run at a temperature of 90 or 100 degrees instead of 60 which is the proper temperature.

When the cold water has been so regulated that the proper temperature is attained, allow the low wines, together with the ether and other foul odors, to run off into the low wine tub.

When the liquor begins to run sweet close cock, D, from the colonette. This opens it on to the column.

Open return cock, d, on to pipe J, which leads through the surface of the still, A, to near its bottom. In the course of about two hours, the alcoholic vapors will pass through the column, the goose, and enter the worm, which condenses them into liquid, and 75 per cent. alcohol will flow from the outlet at the rate of 120 gallons per hour.

As soon as the flow of alcohol commences the water which is used for cooling, must be regulated. That which enters the worm tub serves to reduce the vapors to liquid. The water which enters the goose tub regulates the alcoholic strength of the liquor. While this charge is running off, the other still, AA, is charged, in the same manner as the first. When this is done, the side cock, G, closed, and the screw cap, 5, adjusted.

Change the exhaust valves as follows : Close 2, open 3 and 4. This will conduct the exhaust steam through the coil of still, AA, and will escape through valve 4, into the exhaust tub.

It will be found that by the time the high proof alcohol is run off, through the column, and indicates an increase in temperature, that the liquor in the second still has run off its low wines through the colonette.

At this point two persons are requisite to make the change, one is stationed at three way cock, D, and the other at DD. These two cocks are reversed simultaneously. This action turns the first still, A, on to the colonette, and the second on to the column. The cocks on the return pipes being changed in like manner.

The exhaust valves, as well as those which supply the steam, are then changed.

6 is closed, 7 is opened. 3 and 4 are closed, and 1 and 2 opened.

Then the remains of the first charge is run off as low wines through the colonette, by the heating power which is supplied by the exhausted steam.

When this is accomplished and no more alcoholic substance remains in the first still, A, open side cock, G, open valve, 4, close 1, 2 and 3. Open discharge cock, O, and allow the dregs to run off.

Remove the screw cap, and charge the still anew.

By this means the fine alcohol flows continually day after day without cessation.

It may be remarked that the first passage of the low wines through the colonette and condenser causes a delay of about one hour, and that of the alcohol, another delay of two or more hours. The cause of this is due to the fact that the water in the condenser and goose tubs was cold, and had to be heated by the ascending vapors, to the boiling point of alcohol. When once the water has been heated and is maintained at the proper temperature this difficulty is overcome and the process thereafter continues as long as the two stills are kept in alternate operation.

THE FRENCH CONDENSER.

The construction of this device may be explained as follows :

Two copper cylinders are formed in such a manner that when placed one inside of another there shall be a space of one inch between the two, through which the vapors pass.

Two copper cylinders (See 1, Diagram No. 17), each five feet in length by four feet in breadth with ends contracted four inches cylindrically, and five inches longitudinally (each end), forming the shape of the mouth and neck of a fruit jar. Then a perfectly flat rim, extending from the inner portion of each neck, six inches outwards, is firmly soldered to each end of both cylinders.

These two being ready, two other cylinders 2 and 3 are formed of a uniform diameter. They are each five feet in length by fifty inches in breadth. To one of these, 2, is adjusted a four-inch copper pipe, C, one inch below the upper edge of the cylinder, as it stands on end, and another, D, five inches above the other end, on the reverse side. A one-and-a-half-inch pipe, G, is adjusted at the extreme end of the cylinder on a line with the first four-inch pipe. All of these pipes are made to project twelve inches outwards. This cylinder is placed on the outside of one

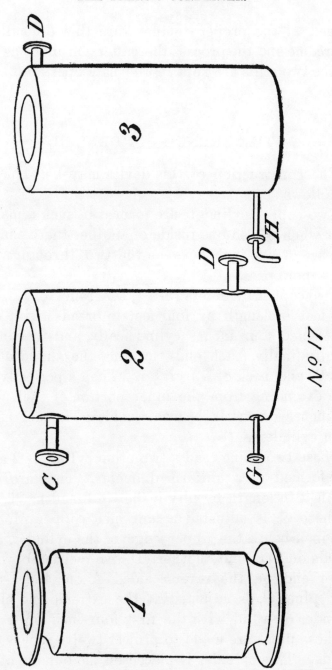

of the contracted ones, 1, and is firmly soldered at both ends, to the extending rims of the inner one.

This then is known as the upper section of the condenser.

The lower section, (See Fig. 3, Diagram No. 17) is formed in like manner, with the exception of the second four-inch pipe, D, which is placed one inch below the upper edge of the cylinder.

Four stout galvanized iron legs, twelve inches in length, are then soldered to the bottom of each section, which are, when in this shape, known as double drums.

The upper section is then placed over the lower one, and the legs soldered to its surface, at the outer edge. (See Diagram No. 18.) In placing these two sections the four-inch pipe which is placed five inches above the bottom of the upper section must be in a diagonal line, over the corresponding pipe which projects from the upper side of the lower section. These two pipes, one of which is the outlet of the upper drum, and the other the inlet of the lower one, are then connected by a four-inch pipe, L, (see Diagram No. 18) bent in a semi-circular form, with a vacuum chamber, E, in the centre, to which is attached a one-inch safety cock, F.

This constitutes the condenser. It is then placed in a tub built for the purpose ; the legs, J, J, J, upon which it rests, are bolted to the bottom of the tub, and the upper surface is secured by means of iron straps which are soldered to the drum, and screwed to the sides of the tub. The pipe connections are made after it is placed in the tub.

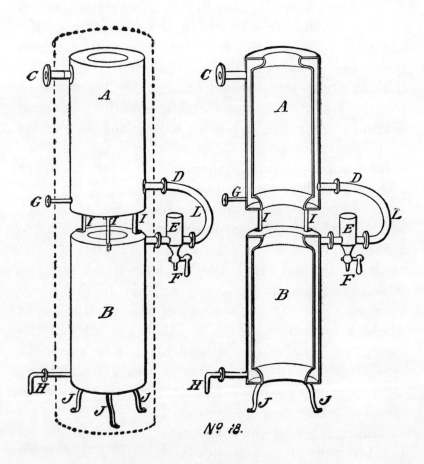

Nº 18.

A circular iron plate is placed over the centre of the bottom of the tub, where the water is let in, in order to force the water to spread as it enters.

When this condenser is connected to the colonette and the vapors enter the upper section, the rotundity of the inner cylinder causes a diversion in three directions. There being but one inch space between the two cylinders, the action of the cold water on both sides causes a rapid condensation of the vapors, which are returned to the colonette in a liquid form.

This continues until the water in the upper portion of the tub becomes heated up to the boiling point of alcohol. At this point the more volatile portion of the vapors pass through the outlet of the upper section into the inlet of the lower section and are there condensed into spirits, called low wines, or feints.

EXPLANATION OF DIAGRAM No. 18.

A, B. Two double cylinders.

C. Inlet.

D. Connecting pipe from upper to lower section.

E. Air chamber (or vacuum).

F. Cock used when necessary to relieve section A, when running foul.

G. Return pipe to convey the condensed liquid back to the colonette.

H. Outlet for alcoholic liquors.

I, I, I. Supports between upper and lower sections.

J, J, J. Three legs upon which the structure rests inside the tub.

THE ACTION OF THE COLUMN.

It has been explained in describing the American column, that the cause of the purification of alcoholic vapors within the column was due to their passage through the water, or condensed liquid, at the bottom of each successive chamber. The present system differs in as much that the action is reversed and the condensed liquid is made to pass through the ascending vapors in the form of rain drops as will be clearly demonstrated.

When the alcoholic vapors pass from the still and enter the lower chamber of the column, they spread and are carried through the perforated plates of the various sections and escape, through the pipe on the dome, into the goose.

The cold water in the goose tub causes the vapors to condense. This condensed liquor is conveyed from the lower curves of the goose, through the return pipe, P, (Diagram No. 16) into the upper portion of the column, and is discharged into the basin, C, (Diagram No. 14) which is placed on the surface of the perforated plate. As this basin over-flows, the liquid spreads over this plate, being prevented from passing through the perforations by the force of the rising vapors. This continues only until the bulk of the liquid has increased to the extent that its weight equals the pressure of the rising vapors.

Here the purifying operation commences, both forces being equalized, the heaviest portion of the liquid as it drops through the perforations falls on the surface of the plate below.

Its lighter substance being again vaporized, ascends with the lightest portion of the rising vapors.

By this means, of one force acting against the other, and with a well regulated steam pressure, the liquid on each plate will attain a uniform depth, of about two inches at the upper section, and gradually increasing on the lower plates up to four inches near the bottom. This however is only temporary. While this dripping, condensing, and re-evaporating is progressing, the water in the goose tub becomes heated ; its condensing power is gradually decreased, and the accumulation of liquid on the upper plates of the column diminishes. This is succeeded by a proportionate decrease on the underlying plates, down to the bottom of the column.

By this time the vapors course their way through the multitudinous bends of the goose and enter the worm, where they are liquidified into alcohol. As soon as the alcohol commences to flow, a stream of cold water is allowed to enter the worm tub, from the centre of its bottom.

This stream is so regulated as to ensure the proper condensation of the alcoholic vapors, which should flow at 60 degrees temperature.

Water is then let in to the goose tub. This must be done with the utmost precaution ; should the flow of water be excessive the alcoholic vapors will condense in the goose, and be returned to the column, thereby causing a cessation of the flow of alcohol ; should the water be inadequate, the vapors will rush through the goose in the same state as they emerge from the column, This increased pressure forces the contents into the worm, completely filling the outlet. The great condensing power of the worm continues to act causing a vacuity between the outlet and the goose connection, the temperature of the running liquor increases rapidly, while the alcoholic strength diminishes. If this continues, the apparatus runs foul, and if not relieved in a short time, the bottom of the still is blown out, or the column bursts. This will serve to illustrate the cause of, and the manner of obviating, this calamity. Should this occur at any time, or while running any kind of a distilling apparatus, there is but one remedy :—Shut off both steam and water, until the apparatus has regained its normal condition.

The colonette acts in precisely the same manner as the column. Its annexed condenser, however, differs from the goose and worm.

As the vapors from the colonette enter the upper portion of the condenser, the space between the two cylinders being but one inch, and the condenser being immersed in cold water,—the condensation is much more rapid than that produced by the goose or worm. The condensed liquor drops to the bottom of the upper section and is returned to the colonette, while the more volatile vapors pass through pipe D, (Diagram No. 18) to the lower section, and are condensed into low wines.

These two double cylinders, which constitute the condenser, are usually placed in one tub, and the cold water introduced from the centre of the bottom, thus the fresh water as it enters, spreads, and forces the surface water as it becomes overheated, to overflow from the side of the upper portion of the tub, where a tin leader is placed for the purpose of conveying it to the exhaust tub. In some cases, however, where the ceiling is not of a sufficient height to admit a tub of such dimensions, the two double cylinders are placed in separate tubs and on two different floors, the connecting pipes passing through the flooring.

THE EPROUVETTE.

Old fashioned distillers receive the liquors as they flow from the outlet, called the tail of the worm, into what is known as the distributing box. This consists of a common square copper box which is attached to the side of the worm tub, at the place where the lower portion of the worm passes through the tub.

Various pipes lead from the bottom of this box to different receiving tubs. The strength of the running liquor is ascertained, by dipping it from the box, immersing a hydrometer in it, and at the same time plunging a thermometer in the liquor to find its temperature. The adoption of the device known as the eprouvette dispenses with this tedious method.

The eprouvette is composed of two copper pots one inside of another. The large one, B, (Diagram No. 19) being twelve inches in height by eight inches diameter. The inner one, A, fifteen inches in height by six inches across. These two pots contain but one bottom. The inner pot has an out-turned lip, K, extending half an inch and reaching around one-half the circumference of the rim. This double pot is

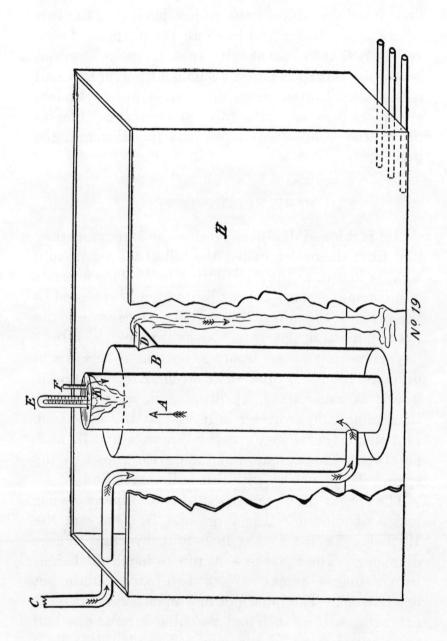

placed in the distributing box, resting on the centre of its bottom.

A pipe, C, leads from the outlet of the worm and passes through the end of the box near its top and through the sides of both the outer and inner pots near their bottom. A spout, D, is formed on the side of the outer pot, two inches below the upper edge, opposite the inlet pipe. A thermometer, E, fastened on a wooded frame is suspended to the back edge on the inside of the inner pot, opposite the out-turned lip. A hook which is fastened to the exact centre of the back of this instrument and bent to fit the edge of the pot, serves to keep it in position. As the liquor flows from the worm, it enters the inner pot and overflows over the lip K, into the outer, from whence it is carried through the spout D, into the distributing box H.

As soon as the liquor begins to flow, the hydrometer, F, is immersed in the alcohol, where it remains during the run of the whole charge. Thus indicating the strength and temperature of the running liquor at all times.

FACTS ABOUT ALCOHOL.

It may be interesting to some of the readers of this book to know that of all liquids known to science, be they natural or artificial, crude or refined, dense or rarified, alcohol (next to water) is the most wonderful, the most perplexing, the most subtle, and yet the most flexible, and its uses the most diversified.

Its scope as a useful as well as a destructive agent appears to be unlimited.

THE PROPERTIES OF ALCOHOL.

Alcohol is a light, transparent, colorless fluid, very mobile, highly volatile and inflammable; when hydrated, it burns with a pale blue and smokeless flame; but when anhydrous, the flame is whitish, and deposits carbon on a cold body.

It mixes in all proportions with water, undergoing no chemical change, and therefore easily separated again from water. In its mixture with water heat is evolved and temporary expansion, but ultimate condensation when the normal temperature is restored; this condensation, however, only occurs when water is present in certain proportions; when it exceeds these the mixture undergoes sensible expansion.

Its mixture with water exhibits a higher specific gravity than the mean of its constituents. This, according to Rudberg, is greatest when 53.739 volumes of alcohol are mixed with 49.386 volumes of water at 59 degrees Fahr., the resulting compound measuring only 100 volumes, and having a specific gravity of 0.927.

Anhydrous alcohol boils at 173.1 degrees Fahr. When diluted with water, its boiling point rises in proportion to the amount of water added.

Alcohol has never been frozen. At 166 degrees below zero it becomes of the consistence of castor oil, but does not solidify. Between 15 degrees below zero and 99 degrees above, it expands with great regularity at the rate of .00047 part of its volume for every degree of rise in temperature. At other temperatures its expansion is anomalous.

TESTS FOR ALCOHOL.

Pure alcohol is colorless ; is neutral to test paper; evaporates entirely by heat, leaving no residuum ; its boiling point should never be below 170 degrees Fahr.

Fusel oil, if present in alcohol, will be discovered by the use of nitrate of silver, in the following manner :—Dissolve 10 grains nitrate of silver in 1 ounce pure distilled water. Into half a tumblerful of the alcohol drop 25 drops of the nitrate solution. If fusel oil is present, a black powder will be found floating on the surface. To make this test effectual, it may sometimes be necessary to wait some hours before examining the result, under exposure to a strong light, in order to discover the least traces of fusel oil.

Its presence may also be detected by half-filling a test tube with alcohol, and slowly filling up the tube with pure concentrated sulphuric acid. Impure spirit will become colored in proportion to the amount of fusel oil in the alcohol.

A very effective test of the strength of alcohol is based on its strong affinity for chloroform. By using a graduated glass tube, a measured quantity of chloroform is introduced, and a given quantity of alcohol is added. When well mixed together and then left to subside, the chloroform takes up the pure alcohol, and the water, being lighter than chloroform, will float on the top. It will be understood that to make this test effectual, the quantity of chloroform must be large in comparison with the amount of the alcohol to be tested.

For all general purposes, the specific gravity of alcohol will be a correct test of its actual strength.

PHYSICAL EFFECTS OF ALCOHOL.

That alcohol is beneficial to health under certain conditions is attested by the numerous prescriptions which contain it, in whole or in part, which are issued by learned physicians both here and abroad.

The proof that it is a malignant destroyer may be found everywhere. Not only among the poor outcast and habitual inebriates who have passed the boundary line and have become irreclaimable drunkards, but among the wealthy or well-to-do denizens of our land; and what is somewhat surprising is the fact that many of its slaves are men of high social and professional repute.

Alcohol is a fantastical fluid replete with capricious freaks. It is soothing, and yet exciting. It is reliable when properly employed, and withal a veritable fiend robed in the guise of a saint, ever ready to lure its victims to mental, if not bodily destruction, should they be so unfortunate as to overstep the safety mark.

This however need not detract from its many good qualities, nor can it efface its virtues.

This enigmatic fluid may be looked upon as the most astonishing curative substance known to science and an inestimable boon to the human family.

It may appear somewhat ludicrous, although it is

an everyday occurrence, that the medical faculty in general, while condemning the promiscuous use of alcohol (a commendable action on their part), are in the constant habit of prescribing it to their patients.

To some, light wines ; to others, heavy wines, or bottled ales and porter, and in many instances brandy, rum, whiskey, etc.

As a rule when prescribing strong liquors, the attending physician will remark, " get the best French brandy," knowing full well (or he should know), that in ninety-nine cases out of a hundred, pure French brandy is unprocurable.

Why French brandy should take precedence over other liquors of the same alcoholic strength is a question that medical men find rather difficult to answer. They may, if disposed to be communicative, inform you in a confidential manner that there is something about French brandy that does not exist in other alcoholic liquors.

What is that something?

It is an acknowledged fact, authenticated by our most celebrated chemists, that alcohol, no matter from what source it may be obtained, whether from grapes, apples, pears, peaches, cane sugar, wheat, corn, rye or other vegetation, is identically the same in every respect, that is to say, when freed from its impurities.

What are its impurities?

Fusel oil, with minute particles of acids, sugar, glycerine, tannin, etc.

It has also been demonstrated that fusel oil is the chief offensive ingredient, and that it exists in all unrectified spirituous liquors. Thus, the benefits to be obtained when strong liquors are prescribed may be attributable to the alcoholic portion of the dose.

Whence then comes this tendency to discriminate in favor of the French rather than the American product, when both possess like qualifications?

These remarks are not intended to apply to wines, beer, ales or porter, which are known to possess invigorating properties, but are confined to distilled products.

ALCOHOL AS AN ANTISEPTIC.

There are three powerful antiseptic substances used throughout the civilized world for various purposes, one of which purposes and an important one, is their aptitude in preventing decay in other bodies.

These three substances are known as *Alcohol, Sugar,* and *Vinegar.*

One only of these three may be viewed as a natural product, and that only partially so, since starch is convertible into sugar. It may be worthy of notice that sugar, alcohol and vinegar—all three emanating from one source—act upon organic bodies with nearly equal force in preventing decay.

Compare this with the fact that the starchy envelope which surrounds the germ contained in every seed is capable of preserving its vitality for thousands of years. It may then be possible for the attentive observer to form some conception of the power which not only exists, but is in a manner indestructible, in this saccharine family, over which even the action of fire only serves to set the component atoms free, that they may rejoin and take part in elementary systems and assist nature in reproducing similar plants or seeds.

ALCOHOL AS A STIMULANT.

It has been demonstrated how, when sugar has undergone what appears to be a complete transformation, the beneficial portion remains, or more properly speaking, is transferred to the newly formed substance—Alcohol.

It has been shown that alcohol is the basis of all wines, beer, ales, porter, bitters and other stimulants; it has been proved that alcohol is the life and the preserver of these various liquids, without which the whole fabric would fall to decay.

In the face of all this, who is there bold enough to aver that alcohol when properly employed is not as beneficial to the system as sugar or bread?

A surfeit of either will cause excruciating pain and distress. The numerous ailments which are the direct results of over eating outnumber those that are due solely to the use of alcholic substances.

The action of alcohol upon the nerves is that of a stimulant. It excites them according to the quantity taken, at times to an unnatural degree of activity.

This heightened action is carried to the heart, causing it to beat with greater force, thus quickening the circulation of the blood; the stimulus is thereby conveyed to the brain.

When alcohol is taken in small quantities it serves as a moderate excitant. It gives tone to the mental faculties and promotes mirth and merriment.

When taken in large quantities the effect changes

The sense of exaltation gives way to moroseness; disagreeable thoughts flash through the brain, the intellect is weakened, images and fantastical ideas succeed each other with bewildering rapidity. The brain whirls ; the victim loses his balance and falls.

If left alone, the office of the brain relaxes its functions and a state of torpor resembling sleep follows, after which a sickly reaction takes place lasting from one to five days. This however is not always the case. There are instances when from the very moment of imbibing the first potion a sensation as if of hatred seems to overpower every good feeling. The victim imagines himself at enmity with some imaginary foe, resents every offer to tranquilize his mind. To use a slang phrase, "he is full of fight"; and unless some friend knocks him down and conveys him home he is very apt to commit a treacherous act or assault on some inoffensive creature usually weaker than himself. Curious as it may seem this state of inebriety gives rise to the same low cunning that is so remarkable among the insane. No amount of intoxicants will suffice to subdue the animal strength of this class of inebriates.

Neither in appearance nor demeanor can the least sign of alcoholism be discerned.

None but habitual drinkers are ever affected in the manner just described. It appears that alcohol acts with unequal intensity upon different parts of the nervous system. It makes choice of certain regions of the brain. This is proven by the unequal excitement which is produced upon different persons of diverse temperament.

In one, it stimulates energetical powers of action and thought; in another, it excites jealousy and envy; a third is surfeited with vanity and egotism; a fourth becomes demented; the fifth, jocose and merry.

People with harsh and discordant voices imagine themselves vocalists; orators without eloquence, misers who become spendthrifts, as well as wise men who make fools of themselves, may all be considered in this same category.

ADULTERATION OF LIQUORS, ETC.

The system of adulterating wines and liquors is not, as is generally supposed, confined to the production of the lower grades of beverages. On the contrary it is known to be a universal custom, and is in many instances of great benefit to the wine or liquor so manipulated, as by this means the offensive ingredients which form part of the wine or liquor become modified or neutralized.

French brandies of every description, from Cognac to La Rochelle, undergo more or less adulteration.

Some of these brandies are too high flavored, others are almost devoid of these qualities.

Some are remarkably astringent while a large portion are what is termed flat. There appears to exist some peculiarity in all brands by which they are easily distinguishable, especially by experts.

These various crude products are usually conveyed to some one or other seaport where the blending is consummated. Large quantities of alcohol enter into this blending process ; in many cases ten parts of reduced alcohol to two parts of the mixed brandies.

The greater portion of alcohol that is exported from the United States to France is returned to us as French brandy. It must be admitted that there are a few exceptions; these however do not benefit the public in general, as they are confined to private importations.

This may appear strange. Nevertheless when the cause is made apparent it may be more readily understood.

Newly distilled brandies are without exception harsh, rank, disagreeable and in some cases noxious (the same may be said of all other alcoholic liquors); where it is practicable to allow these to repose a few years they become mellow and what is usually termed ripe. The wood in which they are stored, usually oak or ash, seems to absorb the offensive odors and at the same time supply an astringent (tannin). Producers cannot afford to wait so long a time, and there being no demand from consumers for the newly distilled liquors, they are obliged to dispose of their product to what we in this country call *Compounders*, or *Rectifiers*, and in France *Fabricants*, or (vulgarly) *empoisonneurs*, which means poisoners. These experts by means of art and artifice will produce in a few days an article that will compare favorably with from four to six year old brandy ; and were the two offered to any, save an expert, the preference would invariably be in favor of the mixture rather than the pure, but new distillate.

There is a strange peculiarity about mixing alcoholic

liquors that is not generally understood ; or, if understood, is often overlooked. It is this :—

When alcohol and water are united, it is generally assumed that if one hundred gallons of 95 per cent. alcohol and an equal quantity of water are mixed (both being at a temperature of 60 degrees Fahr.) that the amount and strength of the mixture will be two hundred gallons of proof liquor. So positive are a good many liquor dealers of this that it is doubtful whether or not the following explanation will suffice to convince them of their error.

100 gallons of 95 per cent. alcohol contain

95 gallons absolute alcohol.

5 gallons water.

Add to this 100 gallons of water and we obtain a mixture composed of 105 gallons of water to 95 gallons absolute alcohol. This proves that, in order to obtain standard proof liquor, ten and one-twentieth of a gallon of alcohol must be added to the first two hundred gallons, in order to offset the ten gallons of surplus water.

The cause of this error is easily explained. When alcohol and water are united heat is generated. This is caused by friction. The friction is due to the commotion which is set in motion by the chemical action of the alcohol on the water, or the water on the alcohol as the case may be.

The mixture for a few hours will show a fictitious alcoholic strength. It may be observed, however, that it has in the meantime, and while undergoing the process, gained a corresponding degree of temperature ; both of which disappear after standing a day or two.

SHRINKAGE IN ALCOHOLIC LIQUORS.

Shrinkage in liquors is generally attributable to evaporation.

There has in all probability been more discussions on this point than on all other alcoholic mysteries combined.

A merchant buys a cask of mixed liquor. He sees it filled and gauged ; the mixing has been done in his presence. The proof is standard. The cask is filled up to the bung. He seals it and sees it shipped, or carts it off in his own wagon. It is safely deposited in his own cellar. The next day, or the day following he is surprised to find that a shortage of from one-half, to one-and-a-half gallons exists, depending on the size of the cask. Not only this but the proof is found far below what he bargained for.

As regards the proof, it has already been explained ; the shortage, or the cause of it, has never been fully explained.

That it is due to the action of the alcoholic portion of the liquor has been ascertained through various experiments among which may be mentioned the following :

Take one gallon of alcohol ; weigh it to make sure that none is lost. Pour it carefully into a two-gallon graduated bottle, fitted with ground glass stopper. Add to this one gallon of pure water, both being at a temperature of 60 degrees Fahrenheit ; next, weigh the bottle with its contents after closing it, so that no vapor can by any means escape; then note upon which of the graduated marks the surface of the liquid stands, after being well shaken. The full proof will be indicated by the uniform circle of globules, known as a full bead, which surrounds the surface of the liquor. Allow this to stand, say forty-eight hours, and it will be found that the bulk has decreased from two to three per cent., and yet the weight has neither increased nor diminished.

This gives rise to the belief that alcohol is composed of myriads of globular atoms, which are either porous, or hollow, such as water or yeast bubbles. The orifice in either case being so diminutive that it impedes the water from filling the cavity, which it eventually does by first expelling or absorbing the gas which the bubbles contain.

CHEMICAL COMPOSITION OF ALCOHOL.

The source and foundation of alcohol is a radical, known to science as Ethyl ; this is implanted by nature. Ethyl is the root, the origin, or basis of all alcoholic fabrics.

It is composed of two gases, known as *Carbonic acid*, and *Hydrogen.*

By adding to these two gases five per cent. of another gas, known as *Oxygen*, the combination becomes an Oxide, so called on account of its being impregnated with oxygen. This is known to chemists and to science as the Hydrated Oxide of Ethyl and to liquor dealers and the public as 95 per cent.

alcohol, which term indicates that it contains 95
parts of absolute alcohol, to 5 parts of water (or
oxygen, as water is composed of eight-ninths of this
gas). It will be seen therefore that the composition
of alcohol is as follows :

Carbonic acid, four parts.

Hydrogen, five parts.

Oxygen, within a fraction of five per cent.

For the benefit of those of our readers who wish to
pursue their researches further into the labyrinth of
this preplexing investigation, a brief summary of the
elementary bodies such as enter into, or take part in
the formation of spirituous liquors, has been prepared
with the utmost care, and with a view to instruct
those who are not familiar with organic matter.

CARBON.

As has been remarked carbon is a component part
of alcohol.

Carbonic acid is the highest known oxide of carbon.

This gas is inodorous, colorless and elastic. It
extinguishes fire, and is so poisonous that a small
quantity of it mixed with the atmospheric air we
inhale destroys life.

Water absorbs this gas from the atmosphere, and
it is owing to its presence in spring and well water
that we are indebted to their pleasant flavor.

The poisonous quality of this gas is a striking
instance of the change which is produced on bodies
by chemical combinations. Charcoal, which is pure
carbon, can be taken into the stomach with impunity,
and is not injurious to the lungs.

Oxygen as it exists in the atmosphere can be inhaled without any ill effects, but when the two substances are chemically united, they form a compound of the most deadly poison which when inhaled destroys life almost instantaneously.

HYDROGEN.

This gas, which also forms a basis of alcohol, is transparent and tasteless, and is the lightest gas known.

Hydrogen is never found free in nature but exists in water, constituting one-ninth of its weight.

It is an essential constituent of all organized substances, vegetable and animal. It is abundantly supplied to water-plants. Although the lightest of all gases scientists pronounce it a metal.

OXYGEN.

Oxygen is the most important of the elements. It is in some way concerned in nearly all chemical changes, and in most of them it takes a very prominent part.

The condition of oxygen is that of gas, resembling common air, (which is a mixture of several gases).

Some gases when exposed to great cold are brought down to a liquid, and even a solid state, others are condensed to a liquid by pressure, but no degree of cold or pressure ever yet applied, has been able to overcome or destroy the gaseous properties of oxygen.

Chemical force alone can do this. Oxygen is transparent, colorless, tasteless and inodorous.

It is about one-tenth heavier than air, and possesses the same mechanical properties. It acts neither as an acid nor an alkali · and is dissolved sparingly by water.

Oxygen is the most widely diffused of all the elements. It constitutes one-fifth by weight of the atmosphere, eight-ninths of the ocean and all other waters, nearly one-half of the solid rocks that compose the crust of the globe. Every solid substance we see around us, the houses in which we live, the stones and ground upon which we stand, and more than one-half of the bodies of all living animals and plants are composed of this chief of elements. The discovery of oxygen was made by Doctor Priestly in 1774 and it has been justly pronounced the chief discovery of the last century.

It disclosed the phenomena of nature in an entirely new aspect. It exploded the old theories and laid the foundation of modern chemical science.

Oxygen has a very wide range of combination. It unites with all the elements (except *Fluorine*) forming compounds termed oxides. The act of combination is called oxidation.

The leading property of oxygen is the intense energy with which it unites with other substances.

So vehement is this action that fire is produced and hence oxygen is the supporter of combustion. All substances which burn in the air, burn in pure oxygen gas with greatly increased brilliancy. The light and heat are produced by the chemical union of the oxygen with the burning body.

All the common cases of combustion which take

place in the air are due to the same cause, the combination of its oxygen with combustible substances ; it here proceeds in a more subdued and regulated way, because atmospheric oxygen is diluted with four times its bulk of another gas which if taken alone extinguishes fire altogether. Common cases of combustion depend upon the quantity of oxygen consumed and not upon the amount of the combustible with which it unites. The affinity of oxygen is exerted at low temperatures as well as at high ones ; its activity never ceases ; it exists in a free state throughout the atmosphere which envelops the globe and is in constant contact with all forms of matter, attacking everything with which it is not already combined.

The cause of decay in vegetable and animal substances is the action of oxygen upon the elements of which they consist. They are oxidized, that is to say, they undergo a slow combustion which breaks them up into simpler and more permanent compounds.

Oxidation is also the grand process by which air, earth and sea are cleansed and purified ; putrid vapors and pestilential effluvia are destroyed by a process of burning, more slowly indeed but as really as if it were done in a furnace.

Oxygen is the real sustainer of life. The most interesting relations of oxygen are those which refer to the animal kingdom. It is the universal supporter of respiration, and as this is a vital process, it is a supporter of life.

According to scientific reports the lungs of land

animals and the gills of fish, are both adapted to the same purpose, and that is to absorb oxygen, the one from the air, the other from water. An animal confined in a given bulk of air, after having consumed its oxygen, dies. If confined in the same bulk of free oxygen it lives about three times as long.

The chemical action that takes place is simple oxidation, the same that occurs in the open combustion of fuel except that it is in a less intense degree. The oxygen combines with the elements of the body, oxidising or burning them, and the products of the combustion pass from the system by the various natural channels.

Its action upon the living system is the same as upon dead matter, purely destructive! It enters the lungs, is absorbed by the blood, and carried to every part where blood vessels are to be found. Every organ, tissue, muscle, nerve, and membrane is wasted away; burnt to poisonous gases and ashes, and thrown from the system as dead and useless matter. Such is the relation of oxygen to all the animal races that inhabit the earth.

Its action is essentially and always destructive, and yet it is the sustainer of life, the main spring of all vital activity. If this be the case, it may be asked: "If this destroying agent enshrouds the globe, and its office be thus only to burn and destroy, why does it not at once reduce all combustible things to ashes and the earth to desolation?"

The answer to the question is this:

The rays of the sun are the great antagonists of oxygen; under their influence the mineral elements are changed to living forms.   While under the influence of oxygen they are returned again to the inorganic world.   If oxygen delapidates, the sun's rays renovate.   If it decomposes and breaks down, they construct and build up.   If oxygen is the main spring of destruction on this earth, wasting, burning, consuming and hastening the dissolution of all things, the sun's rays constitute the mighty force of counteraction.   They reunite the dissevered elements, substitute development for decay, and bring forth life from the bosom of death.

WATER.

The most extensively used, and what would of first appear as the most insignificant, and yet is of the utmost importance to the manufacturer or producer, is water.

This substance, were it classified in the same manner as wines or liquors are graded, would compose a greater number of brands than all alcoholic products put together.

To the quality of water may in many cases be attributable either the complete success or utter failure of an undertaking, especially in the production of beer, ale, porter, whiskey, cordials and other alcoholic compounds.

Water like other liquids contains in many instances various impurities, which should be guarded against, destroyed, or neutralized.

Water is composed of two gases ; oxygen and hydrogen.   Eight parts oxygen to one part of hydrogen.

When perfectly pure, water is tasteless and apparently (in small quantities) colorless. It has the power of assuming either the solid, the liquid or the vaporous state, and with equal facility becomes sweet, sour, salt, bitter or poisonous according to whatever substance it may hold in solution.

Water unites with acids and gases, and forms compounds called hydrates, the formation of which are often very remarkable, as in the case of lime and water. As the water combines with the lime, the heat that is produced is so great that it ignites wood. Vessels laden with lime have been set on fire through a small leak allowing water to come in contact with the lime. The cause of this tremendous heat is due to the water being transformed from a liquid to a solid state.

When the impurities which are contained in water consist of gases that may be more or less offensive, these may be removed by boiling.

Rain water away from large cities is the purest water to be found and the best calculated for malting, mashing, brewing, or compounding.

This is easily explained. As the rain falls it passes through the natural gases that exist in the air, but when it falls over a city, or is filtered through the soil and the crevices of rocks, it becomes contaminated with the foul gases that rise from the tainted city in the one case, or is impregnated with various earthy salts on the other. As a rule, river water contains the least of these salts or objectionable gases.

HARD WATER.

Water derives its quality of hardness from the presence of salts of lime. One grain of sulphate of lime will convert two thousand grains of soft water into hard water.

Common soap when put into hard water, instead of dissolving, as it does in soft water, will curdle ; that is to say, the soap is partly decomposed and a new soap is formed which contains lime as a basis instead of potash or soda.

This new formation, or combination, will not dissolve, and may be seen on the surface of the water in the form of greasy scum, and adheres to whatever it touches.

This is the case when hard water is employed in preparing compounds ; the lime destroys whatever it meets that is antagonistic, and failing to destroy, neutralizes by combining even at the loss of its own identity.

SURE TEST FOR HARD WATER.

In locating a distilling works, it is of great importance to ascertain the quality of water on the premises, The best method is to dissolve a little soap in alcohol. then pour a few drops of this solution in the water to be examined. If it remains clear, the water is soft ; if it turns muddy, then the water is hard.

Some waters are more or less impregnated with various substances such as salts of iron, sulphur, soda, magnesia, etc. These waters are known as mineral waters. One of the celebrated Saratoga springs is said to flow with water charged with hydriodate of soda, carbonate of soda, carbonate of magnesia, carbonate of lime, carbonate of iron, silex and alumina.

PURIFYING WATER.

Water is best purified by distillation. Boiling kills all the animal and vegetable matter; it expels the foul gases and precipitates carbonate of lime. It is this carbonate which is found incrusting the interior of boiling kettles, steam boilers, etc.

THE POWER OF WATER.

When water freezes, it expands very much, and exerts so great a force as to burst the strongest pipes, through which it flows easily in liquid form. It will crumble the surface of the hardest rocks.

Its power when vaporized and converted into steam is too well known to need comment.

The action of the two powerful agencies, heat and cold, is here conspicuously exhibited.

PROOF SPIRITS AND PERCENTAGE.

The strength of spirits is usually ascertained by Tralles' Hydrometer, which is graded from 0 (pure water at 60° Fahr.), up to 100 (pure anhydrous alcohol at 60°. The immersion of the hydrometer denotes the percentage of alcoholic strength.

There are two methods in use by which the strength of spirits is designated. Ordinary spirits may be of any *percentage* ; a liquid which consists of 20 parts out of 100 ($\frac{1}{5}$) spirit and 80 parts ($\frac{4}{5}$) water would naturally be designated as 20 per cent., etc.

A liquid consisting of 50 parts ($\frac{1}{2}$) spirit and 50 parts ($\frac{1}{2}$) water is therefore 50 per cent. which is also called *Proof Spirits.*

It follows, that a liquid of a higher percentage than 50, would be *above proof ;* and of a lower percentage than 50, would be *below proof.*

In estimating the strength of alcohol, proof (or 50 per cent.) is sometimes assumed as the basis, and is designated by 100 as the unit of proof strength.

Inasmuch as 100 proof represents 50 per cent., and pure anhydrous alcohol is 100 per cent., the difference between 50 and 100 would be represented by an additional 100 degrees of proof, or, 100 *per cent.* is the same as 200 *proof.*

Simple arithmetic, therefore, demonstrates that, for instance :

As 50 per cent. = 100 proof.
Then 55   "   = 110 proof.
       60   "   = 120 proof.
       75   "   = 150 proof.
       90   "   = 180 proof.
       95   "   = 190 proof.
       100   "   = 200 proof.

TO FIND THE PERCENTAGE EQUIVALENT TO ANY GIVEN
PROOF.

Deduct 100 from the given proof, halve it, and add that half to 50 ; the result is the equivalent percentage.

Thus, to find the equivalent percentage of spirits of 160 proof,

160—100=60.   60 divided by 2=30.

50+30 =80, the required percentage.

TO FIND THE EQUIVALENT PROOF OF ANY GIVEN PERCENTAGE.

Deduct 50 from the given percentage, double it, and add the quotient to 100 :

Thus, to find the equivalent proof of 80 per cent. spirits :

80—50=30.   30×2=60.   100+60=160, the required proof.

It will be understood that alcohol ceases to be alcohol when *below* proof, it is then *low wines*, or *diluted alcohol*.

The shrinkage in *bulk*, which occurs in the mixing of alcohol and water, has already been mentioned on page 136 of this work, but the *weight* of the mixture remains the same as the combined weight of the two component parts.

In proof spirits, at a temperature of 60 degrees Fahrenheit, the proportions by *weight* of alcohol and water are 100 parts of alcohol and 103.08 parts of water ; their combined *weight* being 203.08 parts, and showing a specific gravity of .91984.

In the same proof spirits, the proportions in *bulk* are 100 measures of alcohol and 81.80 measures of water ; in combination, however, their resultant bulk is only 175.23 measures. If the mixture had undergone no shrinkage, its specific gravity would be about .8862, but the diminution in bulk raises its specific gravity to .91984.

TABLE OF PERCENTAGE BY VOLUME OF ALCOHOL, WITH
EQUIVALENT PERCENTAGE BY WEIGHT, AND
CORRESPONDING SPECIFIC GRAVITY.

Tralle Per cent. by Volume.	Per cent. by Weight.	Specific Gravity 60° Fahr.	Tralle Per cent. by Volume.	Per cent. by Weight.	Specific Gravity 60° Fahr.	Tralle Per cent. by Volume.	Per cent. by Weight.	Specific Gravity 60° Fahr.
0	0	.9991	34	28.12	.9596	68	60.37	.8941
1	0.79	.9976	35	28.99	.9583	69	61.43	.8917
2	1.59	.9961	36	29.86	.9570	70	62.49	.8892
3	2.39	.9947	37	30.74	.9556	71	63.56	.8867
4	3.20	.9933	38	31.62	.9541	72	64.64	.8842
5	4.00	.9919	39	32.50	.9526	73	65.72	.8817
6	4.81	.9906	40	33.39	.9510	74	66.82	.8791
7	5.61	.9893	41	34.28	.9494	75	67.93	.8765
8	6.42	.9881	42	35.18	.9478	76	69.03	.8739
9	7.24	.9869	43	36.08	.9461	77	70.16	.8712
10	8.05	.9857	44	36.98	.9444	78	71.29	.8685
11	8.87	.9845	45	37.90	.9427	79	72.42	.8658
12	9.69	.9834	46	38.81	.9409	80	73.58	.8631
13	10.51	.9823	47	39.73	.9391	81	74.74	.8603
14	11.33	.9812	48	40.65	.9373	82	75.92	.8575
15	12.15	.9802	49	41.58	.9354	83	77.09	.8547
16	12.97	.9791	50	42.52	.9335	84	78.28	.8518
17	13.79	.9781	51	43.46	.9315	85	79.49	.8488
18	14.62	.9771	52	44.41	.9259	86	80.71	.8458
19	15.45	.9761	53	45.36	.9275	87	81.94	.8428
20	16.28	.9751	54	46.32	.9254	88	93.19	.8397
21	17.11	.9741	55	47.29	.9234	89	84.46	.8365
22	17.95	.9731	56	48.25	.9213	90	85.75	.8332
23	18.78	.9720	57	49.22	.9192	91	87.04	.8299
24	19.62	.9710	58	50.21	.9170	92	88.36	.8265
25	20.46	.9700	59	51.20	.9148	93	89.70	.8230
26	21.30	.9689	60	52.20	.9126	94	91.06	.8194
27	22.14	.9679	61	53.19	.9104	95	92.45	.8157
28	22.99	.9668	62	54.19	.9082	96	93.87	.8118
29	23.84	.9657	63	55.20	.9059	97	95.33	.8077
30	24.69	.9646	64	56.22	.9036	98	96.83	.8034
31	25.54	.9634	65	57.25	.9013	99	98.38	.7988
32	26.40	.9622	66	58.28	.8989	100	100.00	.7938
33	27.26	.9609	67	59.32	.8965			

The foregoing table exhibits the percentage by volume of absolute (anhydrous) alcohol in spirits of any given strength ; it gives its equivalent percentage by weight, and its corresponding specific gravity, at a temperature of 60 degrees Fahrenheit.

The percentage by volume of any spirits is ascertained by the use of Tralles' hydrometer ; the number on the scale, to which the hydrometer sinks in the liquid, denotes the percentage by volume, or number of parts in 100, of anhydrous alcohol which the liquid contains.

A liquid in which the hydrometer indicates 43 degrees consists, therefore, of 43 volumes (or parts) of pure alcohol and 57 volumes of water.

Alcohol is fully one-fifth lighter than water, consequently the actual percentage by weight of pure alcohol in any given liquid would be less than its comparative percentage by volume. Referring to the example just quoted, 43 volumes or parts of pure alcohol out of 100 would represent only about 36 parts out of 100 by weight ; so that a liquid which consists of 43 parts by volume of alcohol and 57 parts by volume of water, would be the same as 36.08 parts by weight of alcohol and 63.92 parts by weight of water.

The percentage of alcohol by weight equivalent to any percentage by volume is thus found :—

Multiply the percentage by volume by .7938 (the specific gravity of anhydrous alcohol), and divide the quotient by the specific gravity corresponding to the percentage by volume.

Example : Suppose a quantity of spirits indicates 60 per cent. by volume of pure spirits. The table shows its sp. gr. to be .9126.

.7938 × 60 = 47.6280.

47.6280 ÷ .9126 = 52.20 which is the equivalent percentage by weight.

Specific gravity is the weight of a given measure of any liquid compared with the weight of the same measure of pure distilled water at the temperature of its greatest density, $39\frac{1}{2}°$ Fahrenheit; for ready comparison, the weight of water is represented by the unit 1, the specific gravity of liquids lighter than water being represented by a decimal, usually of four places. Alcohol, for instance, has a specific gravity of .7938.

The above table gives the specific gravity corresponding with each degree indicated on Tralles' hydrometer, at a temperature of 60 degrees Fahrenheit, at which temperature water has a specific gravity of .9991.

It is not always practicable to test a sample of spirits at the regulation temperature of 60 degrees; to meet this difficulty, a test of its percentage may be made at any ordinary temperature, and the true percentage at 60 degrees be approximately obtained, sufficiently correct for general purposes.

The following table will be found useful under such circumstances:

Suppose a sample of spirits to be at a temperature of 45 degrees at which the hydrometer indicates a percentage of about 47; in the column under the head of 45°, we find a percentage of 46.9 (the nearest to the required 47); on a line with the figures 46.9, and on the extreme left (or right) hand column, we find the figures 50. We thus ascertain that 50 is the *true* percentage at 60 degrees, corresponding with 46.9, the *observed* percentage at 45 degrees.

TABLE TO FIND THE TRUE PERCENTAGE OF ABSOLUTE ALCOHOL *by volume in a liquid at 60° from the observed percentage indicated by a Glass Hydrometer at any other temperature.*

60°	30°	35°	40°	45°	50°	55°	65°	70°	75°	80°	85°	60°
0	−0.2	−0.4	−0.4	−0.5	−0.4	−0.2	+0.2	+0.6	+1.0	+1.4	+1.9	0
5	+4.6	+4 5	+4.5	+4.5	+4.6	+4.8	5.3	5.8	6.2	6.7	7.3	5
10	9.1	9.0	9.1	9.2	9 3	9.7	10.4	11.0	11.6	12.3	13.0	10
15	13.0	13.1	13.3	13.5	13.9	14 5	15.6	16.3	17.1	18.0	19.0	15
20	16.5	16 9	17.4	17.8	18.5	19.2	20.8	21.8	22.8	23.8	24 9	20
25	19.9	20.6	21.4	22.2	23.0	24.1	25.9	27.0	28.2	29.4	30.5	25
30	23.5	24.5	25.7	26.6	27.7	28 8	31.1	32.2	33.4	34.5	35.7	30
35	28.0	29.2	30.4	31.6	32.7	33 8	36.2	37.3	38.4	39.5	40.6	35
40	33.0	34.2	35.4	36.7	37.8	39.0	41.1	42.2	43.3	44.3	45.4	40
45	38.4	39.6	40.7	41.8	42.9	43 9	46.1	47.1	48.2	49.2	50.3	45
50	43.7	44.7	45.8	46.9	47.9	49.0	51.0	52.0	53.0	54 0	55.1	50
55	49.0	50 0	51.0	52.0	53.0	54.0	54.9	56.9	57.9	58.9	59.9	55
60	54 2	55.2	56.2	57 1	58.1	59.0	60.9	61.9	62.9	63.8	64.9	60
65	59.4	60 3	61.2	62.2	63.1	64.0	65.9	66.8	67.7	68.6	69.6	65
70	64.6	65.5	66.4	67.3	68.2	69.1	70.8	71.7	72.6	73.5	74.5	70
75	69.8	70 7	71.5	72 4	73.3	74.2	75.8	76.7	77.6	78.4	79.3	75
80	75.0	75 8	76.6	77.5	78.4	79.2	80.8	81.7	82.4	83.2	84 1	80
85	80.3	81.1	81.8	82.6	83.5	84.3	85.7	86.5	87.3	88.0	88.8	85
90	85.6	86.4	87.1	87.9	88.6	89.3	90.7	91.4	92.0	92.7	93.4	90

BEAUMÉ'S HEAVY HYDROMETER.

The strength of saccharine and other liquids heavier than water is generally determined by the use of Beaumé's Heavy Hydrometer. The following table exhibits the specific gravity corresponding with the degrees marked on the hydrometer, beginning at 0 (which indicates pure water at 60 degrees Fahrenheit) and 76 degrees of the scale.

To avoid decimals, the specific gravity of water is here designated by 1000, instead of 1.

SPECIFIC GRAVITY EQUIVALENT TO DEGREES OF BEAUMÉ'S
HEAVY HYDROMETER.

Beaume	Sp Gr.	Beaume	Sp. Gr.	Beaume	Sp. Gr.	Beaume	Sp. Gr.	Beaume	Sp. Gr.
0	1000	16	1125	32	1286	47	1485	62	1758
1	1007	17	1134	33	1298	48	1501	63	1779
2	1014	18	1143	34	1309	49	1516	64	1801
3	1022	19	1152	35	1321	50	1532	65	1823
4	1029	20	1161	36	1334	51	1549	66	1847
5	1036	21	1171	37	1346	52	1566	67	1872
6	1044	22	1180	38	1359	53	1583	68	1897
7	1052	23	1190	39	1372	54	1601	69	1921
8	1060	24	1199	40	1384	55	1618	70	1946
9	1067	25	1210	41	1398	56	1637	71	1974
10	1075	26	1221	42	1412	57	1656	72	2002
11	1083	27	1231	43	1426	58	1676	73	2031
12	1091	28	1242	44	1440	59	1695	74	2059
13	1100	29	1252	45	1454	60	1715	75	2087
14	1108	30	1261	46	1470	61	1736	76	2116
15	1116	31	1275						

TO REDUCE THE STRENGTH OF ALCOHOL.

To find how much water must be added to alcohol of a given strength in order to reduce it to desired lower percentage :

Multiply the number of gallons of spirit by its percentage of strength ; divide the product by the *required* percentage, and deduct 100 from the quotient. The result will be the number of gallons of water to be added to the spirit to reduce it to the percentage sought.

Example :—It is required to reduce 100 gallons of 80 per cent. spirit to 50 per cent., or proof.

$$100 \times 80 = 8000.$$
$$8000 \div 50 = 160.$$
$$160 - 100 = 60.$$

The addition of 60 gallons of water will reduce the strength of the 100 gallons of spirit from its original 80 per cent. to the required 50 per cent.

The following table will show still more correctly the volumes of water that must be added to 100 volumes of spirit of a given percentage, to reduce it to a required lower percentage.

Desired strength in per cent.	90	85	80	75	70	65	60	55	50
85	6.56								
80	13.79	6 83							
75	21.89	14.48	7.20						
70	31.05	23 14	15.35	7.64					
65	41.53	33.03	24.66	16.37	8.15				
60	53.65	44.48	35.44	26.47	17.58	8.56			
55	67.87	57.90	48.07	38.32	28.63	19.02	9.47		
50	84.71	73.90	63.04	52.43	41.73	31.25	20 47	10 35	
45	105.34	93.30	81.38	69.54	57.78	46.09	34.46	22.90	11.41
40	130.80	117.34	104.01	90.76	77.58	64.48	51.43	38.46	25.55
35	163 28	148.01	132.88	117.82	102.84	87.93	73.08	58 31	43.59
30	206.22	188.57	171.05	153 61	136.04	118.94	101.71	84.54	67.45
25	266.12	245.15	224.30	203.53	182 83	162.21	141.65	121.16	100.73
20	355.80	329.84	304.01	278.26	252.58	226.98	201 43	175.96	150.55
15	505.27	471.	436.85	402 81	368.83	334.91	301.07	267.29	233.64
10	804.54	753.65	702.89	752.21	601.60	551.06	500.59	450 19	399 85

Example :—Required to reduce 100 gallons of 70 per cent. spirits to 40 per cent. Look on left hand column for 40, the *required* per cent.; on a line to the right, in column under 70 (the *given* percentage), we find 77.58. This shows that a trifle over $77\frac{1}{2}$ gallons of water must be added to reduce the whole to a strength of 40 per cent.

TO INCREASE THE STRENGTH OF ALCOHOL.

To find how much 80 per cent. spirit must be added to spirit of a lower grade, to raise it to a higher grade.

Multiply the number of gallons by the difference between the *required* percentage and the *given* percentage.

Divide this product by the difference between 80 per cent. and *given* percentage. The quotient will be the number of gallons of 80 per cent. spirits to be added, to bring the resulting strength to the required percentage.

Example : To raise 35 gallons of 65 per cent. spirits to a strength of 70 per cent. by the addition of 80 per cent. spirit.

$$70 — 65 = 5.$$
$$5 \times 35 = 175.$$

$$80 — 65 = 15.$$
$$175 \div 15 = 11\tfrac{3}{5}.$$

The addition of $11\tfrac{3}{5}$ gallons of 80 per cent. spirits will raise 35 gallons of 65 per cent. spirit to a strength of 70 per cent. This method will apply equally well where the high grade spirit (here assumed to be 80 per cent.) is at any other high grade or percentage,— 85, or 90, for instance,—by substituting the actual percentage for the 80, and proceeding in the calculation in the same manner.

BOILING HEAT OF SATURATED SOLUTIONS.

There are certain circumstances, especially in distillation with the water-bath, in which a certain temperature is required to be obtained and sustained in order to reach the necessary results. Water alone boils at 212 degrees Fahrenheit, and no higher degree of heat can be reached by it unless confined in a boiler.

By saturating the water with different substances, various higher degrees of heat can be obtained. The following table shows the boiling point of a *saturated* solution of the substances named :

TABLE SHOWING THE BOILING HEAT OF VARIOUS SATURATED
SOLUTIONS.

Muriate of Lime	285?
Acetate of Soda	256
Nitrate of Soda	246
Rochelle Salt	240
Nitre	238
Muriate of Ammonia	236
Tartrate of Potash	234
Sea Salt	224⅓
Muriate of Soda	224
Sulphate of Magnesia	222
Borax	222
Phosphate of Soda	222
Carbonate of Soda	220
Alum	220
Chlorate of Potash	218
Sulphate of Copper	216
Acetate of Lead	215⅓
Glauber Salt	213⅓